Essential Mathematics

Book 9i

David Rayner

Elmwood Press

First published 2002 by
Elmwood Press
80 Attimore Road
Welwyn Garden City
Herts. AL8 6LP
Tel. 01707 333232

British Library Cataloguing in Publication Data

Rayner, David

© David Rayner
The moral rights of the author have been asserted.
Database right Elmwood Press (maker)

ISBN 978 1 902 214 115

Numerical answers are published in a separate book

Artwork by Stephen Hill

Typeset and illustrated by Tech-Set, Gateshead, Tyne and Wear
Printed and bound by WS Bookwell

PREFACE

Essential Mathematics Books *7i*, *8i* and *9i* are written for pupils of 'average' ability in years 7, 8 and 9. Most classrooms contain children with a range of abilities in mathematics. These books are written to cater for this situation.

The author is an enthusiastic supporter of the National Numeracy Strategy. The books have been prepared with the cooperation of teachers and pupils in NNS pilot schools. It is encouraging that most teachers are confident that this more structured approach will help to raise standards of understanding and attainment. There is a comprehensive NNS guide at start of the book with references to all topics.

There is no set path through the books but topics appear in the order suggested in the NNS planning charts. Broadly speaking, parts 1 and 2 can be studied in the Autumn Term, parts 3 and 4 in the Spring Term and parts 5 and 6 in the Summer Term. Part 7 contains material which is beyond the 'core' for KS3 and is intended for study *after* the KS3 tests in May.

The author believes that children learn mathematics most effectively by *doing* mathematics. Many youngsters who find mathematics difficult derive much more pleasure and enjoyment from the subject when they are doing questions which help them build up their confidence. Pupils feel a greater sense of satisfaction when they work in a systematic way and when they can appreciate the purpose and the power of the mathematics they are studying.

No text book will have the 'right' amount of material for every class and the author believes that it is better to have too much material rather than too little. Consequently teachers should judge for themselves which sections or exercises can be studied later. On a practical note, the author recommends the use of exercise books consisting of 7 mm squares.

Opportunities for work towards the 'Using and Applying Mathematics' strand appears throughout the book. Many activities, investigations, games and puzzles are included to provide a healthy variety of learning experiences. The author is aware of the difficulties of teaching on 'Friday afternoons' or on the last few days of term, when both pupils and teachers are tired, and suitable activities are included.

The author is indebted to his co-authors David Allman and Laurence Campbell whose work from the first edition of Essential Mathematics has been included where appropriate. The author would also like to thank his colleagues at school, in particular Christine Godfrey who has written material for this book.

David Rayner

CONTENTS

Using and applying mathematics to solve problems

Applying mathematics and solving problems

2.6
5.4
- Solve increasingly demanding problems and evaluate solutions; explore connections in mathematics across a range of contexts: number, algebra, shape, space and measures, and handling data. Represent problems and sythesise information in algebraic, geometric or graphical form; move from one form to another to gain a different perspective on the problem.

2.2
2.4
- **Solve substantial problems by breaking them into simpler tasks, using a range of efficient techniques, methods and resources, including ICT;** use trial and improvement where a more efficient method is not obvious.

3.2
3.3
5.5
- **Present a concise, reasoned argument, using symbols, diagrams, graphs and related explanatory text; give solutions to problems to an appropriate degree of accuracy.**

5.5
5.6
- Suggest extensions to problems, conjecture and generalise; identify exceptional cases or counter-examples, explaining why.

Numbers and the number system

Place value, ordering and rounding

1.2
- Extend knowledge of integer powers of 10; multiply and divide by any integer power of 10.

3.2
- Use rounding to make estimates; round numbers to the nearest whole number or to one, two or *three* decimal places.

Integers, powers and roots

- Use the prime factor decomposition of a number.

4.5
- Use ICT to estimate square roots and cube roots.

1.1
- Use index notation for integer powers and simple instances of the index laws; *know and use the index laws for multiplication and division of positive integer powers; begin to extend understanding of index notation to negative and fractional powers, recognising that the index laws can be applied to these as well.*

Fractions, decimals, percentages, ratio and proportion

1.5
- Understand the equivalence of simple algebraic fractions; know that a recurring decimal is an exact fraction.

1.5
- Use efficient methods to **add, subtract, multiply and divide** fractions, interpreting division as a multiplicative inverse; cancel common factors before multiplying or dividing.

4.4
- Recognise when fractions or percentages are needed to compare proportions; solve problems involving percentage changes.

4.4
5.3
- **Use proportional reasoning to solve a problem, choosing the correct numbers to take as 100%, or as a whole;** compare two ratios; interpret and use ratio in a range of contexts, including solving word problems.

Calculations

Number operations and the relationships between them

1.2
3.2
- Understand the effects of multiplying and dividing by numbers between 0 and 1; use the laws of arithmetic and inverse operations.

Mental methods and rapid recall of number facts

2.5
- Use known facts to derive unknown facts; extend mental methods of calculation, working with decimals, fractions, percentages, factors, powers and roots, solve word problems mentally.

3.2
- **Make and justify estimates and approximations of calculations.**

Written methods

1.2
- Use standard column procedures to add and subtract integers and decimals of any size, including a mixture of large and small numbers with differing numbers of decimal places; multiply and divide by decimals, dividing by transforming to division by an integer.
For calculations with fractions and percentages, see above.

Calculator methods

2.1
- Use a calculator efficiently and appropriately to perform complex calculations with numbers of any size, knowing not to round during intermediate steps of a calculation; use the constant, π and sign change keys, function keys for powers, roots and fractions, brackets and the memory.

2.1
2.6
5.4
- Enter numbers and interpret the display in context (negative numbers, fractions, decimals, percentages, money, metric measures, time).

Checking results

3.2
- Check results using appropriate methods.

Algebra

Equations, formulae and identities

1.3
- Distinguish the different roles played by letter symbols in equations, identities, formulae and functions.

1.1
- Use index notation for integer powers and simple instances of the index laws.

1.3 • Simplify or transform algebraic expressions by taking out single-term common factors; and simple algebraic fractions.

2.4 • **Construct and solve linear equations with integer coefficients** (with and without brackets, negative signs anywhere in the equation, positive or negative solution), **using an appropriate method**.

7.4 • *Solve a pair of simultaneous linear equations by eliminating one variable; link a graphical representation of an equation or a pair of equations to the algebraic solution; consider cases that have no solution or an infinite number of solutions.*

7.3 • *Solve linear inequalities in one variable, and represent the solution set on a number line; begin to solve inequalities in two variables.*

4.5 • Use systematic trial and improvement methods and ICT tools to find approximate solutions to equations such as $x^3 + x = 20$.

• Solve problems involving direct proportion using algebraic methods, relating algebraic solutions to graphical representations of the equations; use ICT as appropriate.

4.3 • Use formulae from mathematics and other subjects; substitute numbers into expressions and formulae; derive a formula and, in simple cases, change its subject.

Sequences, functions and graphs

4.3 • **Generate terms of a sequence using term-to-term and position-to-term definitions of the sequence, on paper and using ICT.**

4.3 • Generate sequences from practical contexts and **write an expression to describe the *n*th term of an arithmetic sequence**.

5.2 • Find the inverse of a linear function.

5.2 • Generate points and plot graphs of linear
6.3   functions (*y* given implicitly in terms of *x*), e.g. $ay + bx = 0$, $y + bx + c = 0$, on paper and using ICT; **given values for *m* and *c*, find the gradient of lines given by equations of the form $y = mx + c$**.

3.3 • **Construct functions arising from real-life problems and plot their corresponding graphs; interpret graphs arising from real situations**, including distance–time graphs.

Shape, space and measures

Geometrical reasoning: lines, angles and shapes

1.6 • Distinguish between conventions, definitions and derived properties.

1.6 • Explain how to find, calculate and use:
  – the sums of the interior and exterior angles of quadrilaterals, pentagons and hexagons;
  – the interior and exterior angles of regular polygons.

1.6 • **Solve problems using properties of angles, of
7.1   parallel and intersecting lines, and of triangles and other polygons,** justifying inferences and explaining reasoning with diagrams and text; *understand and apply Pythagoras' theorem.*

4.1 • Understand congruence.

1.6 • Know the definition of a circle and the names
1.4   of its parts; explain why inscribed regular polygons can be constructed by equal divisions of a circle.

4.2 • Visualise and use 2-D representations of 3-D objects; analyse 3-D shapes through 2-D projections, including plans and elevations.

Transformations

4.1 • Transform 2-D shapes by combinations of
4.2   translations, rotations and reflections, on paper and using ICT; **know that translations, rotations and reflections preserve length and angle and map objects on to congruent images;** identify reflection symmetry in 3-D shapes.

4.1 • Enlarge 2-D shapes, given a centre of enlargement and a whole-number scale factor, on paper and using ICT; identify the scale factor of an enlargement as the ratio of the lengths of any two corresponding line segments; recognise that enlargements preserve angle but not length, and understand the implications of enlargement for perimeter.

5.3 • Use and interpret maps and scale drawings.

Construction

2.2 • Use straight edge and compasses to construct a triangle, given right angle, hypotenuse and side (RHS); use ICT to explore constructions of triangles and other 2-D shapes.

6.1 • Find the locus of a point that moves according to a simple rule, both by reasoning and by using ICT.

Measures and mensuration

3.1 • Use units of measurement to calculate,
3.4   estimate, measure and solve problems in a variety of contexts; convert between area measures (mm^2 to cm^2, cm^2 to m^2 and vice versa) and between volume measures (mm^3 to cm^3, cm^3 to m^3, and vice versa).

7.2 • *Understand and use measures of speed (and other compound measures such as density or pressure) to solve problems; solve problems involving constant or average rates of change.*

1.4 • **Know and use the formulae for the circumference and area of a circle**.

3.4 • Calculate the surface area and volume of right prisms.

Handling data

Specifying a problem, planning and collecting data

5.5 • Suggest a problem to explore using statistical methods, frame questions and raise conjectures.

5.5 • Discuss how data relate to a problem; identify possible sources, including primary and secondary sources.

5.5 • **Design a survey or experiment to capture the necessary data from one or more sources; determine the sample size and degree of accuracy needed; design, trial and if necessary refine data collection sheets;** construct tables for large discrete and continuous sets of raw data, choosing suitable class intervals; design and use two-way tables.

5.5 • Gather data from specified secondary sources, including printed tables and lists from ICT-based sources.

Processing and representing data, using ICT as appropriate

5.1 • Find summary values that represent the raw data, and select the statistics most appropriate to the problem.

2.3
3.3 • Select, construct and modify, on paper and using ICT, suitable graphical representation to progress an enquiry, including:
  – line graphs for time series;
  – scatter graphs to develop further understanding of correlation;
  identify key features present in the data.

Interpreting and discussing results

3.3
3.5 • Interpret graphs and diagrams and draw inferences to support or cast doubt on initial conjectures; have a basic understanding of correlation.

5.1 • Compare two or more distributions and make inferences, using the shape of the distributions, the range of data and appropriate statistics.

5.5 • **Communicate interpretations and results of a statistical enquiry using selected tables, graphs and diagrams in support,** using ICT as appropriate.

Probability

6.2 • Use the vocabulary of probability in interpreting results involving uncertainty and prediction.

6.2 • Identify all the mutually exclusive outcomes of an experiment; **know that the sum of probabilities of all mutually exclusive outcomes is 1 and use this when solving problems.**

6.2 • Estimate probabilities from experimental data.

6.2 • Compare experimental and theoretical probabilities in a range of contexts; appreciate the difference between mathematical explanation and experimental evidence.

Part 1

1.1 Index laws

- Here are some *square* numbers: $2^2 = 4$ 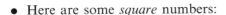 $3^2 = 9$

  Here are some *cube* numbers: $2^3 = 2 \times 2 \times 2 = 8$,
  $3^3 = 3 \times 3 \times 3 = 27$, $10^3 = 10 \times 10 \times 10 = 1000$

- Beyond squares and cubes we say 'to the power of'
  For 3^5 we say 'three to the power of'

  On a calculator, press $\boxed{3}\ \boxed{x^y}\ \boxed{5}\ \boxed{=}$ Answer: 243

  For 7^4 we say 'seven to the power of four'

  On a calculator, press $\boxed{7}\ \boxed{x^y}\ \boxed{4}\ \boxed{=}$ Answer: 2401

Exercise 1

1. Copy and complete this table, using a calculator to help you obtain the answers.

We say	We write	We work out	Answer
2 to the power of 4	2^4	$2 \times 2 \times 2 \times 2$	
1 to the power of 5	1^5	$1 \times 1 \times 1 \times 1 \times 1$	
	6^2		
3 to the power of 4			
	2^6		
10 to the power of 2			
		$5 \times 5 \times 5$	
	6^5		

2. Work out the following:

    (a) 2^5 (b) 1^3 (c) 10^4 (d) 7^2 (e) 0^6

3. Answer true or false:

    (a) $2^2 = 4$ (b) $2^3 = 3^2$ (c) $1^4 = 4$

    (d) $10^2 = 20$ (e) $2^2 + 3^2 = 5^2$ (f) $3^2 + 4^2 = 5^2$

4. Fill in the missing numbers:

    (a) $2^2 = \square$ (b) $3^\square = 27$ (c) $\square^2 = 1$

    (d) $7^\square = 49$ (e) $10^3 = \square$ (f) $\square^4 = 0$

5. Use the $\boxed{x^2}$ button to work out:

    (a) 6^2 (b) 12^2 (c) 20^2 (d) 15^2 (e) 18^2

6. Use the $\boxed{x^2}$ button to work out:

    (a) $1\cdot4^2$ (b) $3\cdot1^2$ (c) $0\cdot8^2$ (d) $5\cdot4^2$ (e) 100^2

    (f) 31^2 (g) $7\cdot5^2$ (h) 200^2 (i) $0\cdot2^2$ (j) $1\cdot25^2$

7. Find the areas of these squares

    (a)   (b)   (c)

                                2.4 cm   7.6 cm

        8 cm

8. Write in index form

    (a) $2 \times 2 \times 2$ (b) $4 \times 4 \times 4 \times 4 \times 4$ (c) $3 \times 3 \times 3 \times 3 \times 3 \times 3 \times 3$

    (d) 9×9 (e) $10 \times 10 \times 10$ (f) $1 \times 1 \times 1 \times 1 \times 1 \times 1 \times 1 \times 1$

9. Write in index form

    (a) $4\cdot5 \times 4\cdot5$ (b) $1\cdot4 \times 1\cdot4 \times 1\cdot4$ (c) $a \times a \times a \times a \times a$

    (d) $p \times p \times p$ (e) $n \times n \times n \times n$ (f) $5 \times 5 \times 3 \times 3 \times 3$

10. Use the $\boxed{x^y}$ button to work out

    (a) 7^3 (b) 2^7 (c) 3^5 (d) 4^3 (e) 10^4

    (f) 3^6 (g) $1\cdot4^3$ (h) $0\cdot1^2$ (i) 3×4^2 (j) $2^3 \times 5^2$

11. Each side of a square field is 110 m long. Work out the area of the field.

Multiplying index numbers

- $3^2 \times 3^3 = (3 \times 3) \times (3 \times 3 \times 3)$
    $= 3 \times 3 \times 3 \times 3 \times 3$
    $= 3^5$

- $4^3 \times 4^4 = (4 \times 4 \times 4) \times (4 \times 4 \times 4 \times 4)$
    $= 4 \times 4 \times 4 \times 4 \times 4 \times 4 \times 4$
    $= 4^7$

> To multiply index numbers with the same base, you *add* the indices.

Exercise 2

1. Copy and complete. Write the answer as an index number.

(a) $2^4 \times 2^3 =$ (b) $4^2 \times 4^5 =$

(c) $5^6 \times 5^2 =$ (d) $3^5 \times 3^5 =$

2. Work out and write the answer as an index number.

(a) $3^6 \times 3^3$ (b) $7^3 \times 7^{10}$

(c) $9^5 \times 9^{50}$ (d) $1^{11} \times 1^{12}$

In Questions **3** to **12** copy and complete.

3. $5^3 \times 5^2 = \square$ **4.** $7^5 \times \square = 7^{11}$

5. $\square \times 3^{10} = 3^{12}$ **6.** $\square \times 8^5 = 8^8$

7. $n^3 \times n^3 = \square$ **8.** $3^{100} \times \square = 3^{102}$

9. $10^2 \times \square = 1000$ **10.** $11^4 \times \square = 11^7$

11. $13^3 \times 13^{30} = \square$ **12.** $a^7 \times \square = a^{20}$

Dividing index numbers

- $3^5 \div 3^2 = \dfrac{3 \times 3 \times 3 \times \cancel{3} \times \cancel{3}}{\cancel{3} \times \cancel{3}}$
    $= 3^3 = 3^{5-2}$

- $7^4 \div 7^1 = \dfrac{7 \times 7 \times 7 \times \cancel{7}}{\cancel{7}}$
    $= 7^3 = 7^{4-1}$

> To divide index numbers with the same base, you *subtract* the indices.

Exercise 3

1. Copy and complete

(a) $4^5 \div 4^2 =$ (b) $6^7 \div 6^3 =$

(c) $5^9 \div 5^3 =$ (d) $3^8 \div 3^2 =$

2. Work out and write the answer as an index number.

(a) $3^8 \div 3^6$ (b) $5^{10} \div 5^7$

(c) $11^{20} \div 11^{11}$ (d) $n^7 \div n^2$

In Questions **3** to **8** copy and complete.

3. $7^4 \div 7^2 = \square$ **4.** $\square \div 2^3 = 2^{11}$

5. $4^9 \div \square = 4^5$ **6.** $\square \div 10^5 = 10^6$

7. $11^{20} \div \square = 11^1$ **8.** $7^{13} \div 7^7 = \square$

9. (a) Look at these calculations:

     $5^2 \div 5^2 = 5^0$, $25 \div 25 = 1$ so $5^0 = 1$

     $2^4 \div 2^4 = 2^0$, $16 \div 16 = 1$ so $2^0 = 1$

(b) Copy and complete:

     (i) $3^3 \div 3^3 = 3^0 = \square$

     (ii) $5^4 \div 5^4 = 5^0 = \square$

     (iii) 'For any number n (apart from $n = 0$) $n^0 = \square$'.

10. Work out.

(a) 7^0 (b) 11^0 (c) $2 \cdot 5^0$ (d) 135^0

11. Use the $\boxed{x^y}$ button on a calculator to work out,

(a) 9^0 (b) 13^0 (c) $11 \cdot 7^0$

12. Look at these calculations:

     $2^2 \div 2^3 = 2^{-1}$, $4 \div 8 = \frac{1}{2}$ so $2^{-1} = \frac{1}{2}$

     $10^2 \div 10^3 = 10^{-1}$, $100 \div 1000 = \frac{1}{10}$ so $10^{-1} = \frac{1}{10}$

(a) Use the $\boxed{x^y}$ button to work out $2^{-1}, 3^{-1}, 4^{-1}, 5^{-1}, 10^{-1}$.

(b) Copy and complete this sentence;

     'n^{-1} means the same as _____.'

Square roots

- A square has an area of 289 cm².
  How long is a side of the square?
  In other words, what number *multiplied* by *itself* makes 289?
  The answer is the *square root* of 289.

  On a calculator press 289 √ .

  The side of the square is 17 cm. [Check $17 \times 17 = 289$]

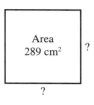

- Most numbers do not have an exact square root.

  Here is a square of area 286 cm².
  To find the length of a side of the square work out √286.

  On a calculator press 286 √ .

  The calculator shows 16·911535.
  To one decimal place, the side of the square is 16·9 cm.

286 cm²

Exercise 4

1. Work out without a calculator:
   (a) $\sqrt{25}$ (b) $\sqrt{49}$ (c) $\sqrt{100}$ (d) $\sqrt{1}$ (e) $\sqrt{81}$

2. Find the sides of these squares

   (a) Area = 16 cm²
   (b) Area = 9 cm²
   (c) Area = 121 cm²

3. Use a calculator to find the following, correct to 1 d.p.
   (a) $\sqrt{20}$ (b) $\sqrt{15}$ (c) $\sqrt{8·3}$ (d) $\sqrt{516}$ (e) $\sqrt{1273}$
   (f) $\sqrt{0·74}$ (g) $\sqrt{0}$ (h) $\sqrt{0·038}$ (i) $\sqrt{58^2}$ (j) $\sqrt{17^2}$

4. A square tile has an area of 50 cm². Find the length of each side of the tile correct to the nearest mm.

5. A square table has an area of 15 000 cm². Find the length of each side of the table correct to the nearest cm.

6. Each small square on a 'mini' chess board has an area of 12 cm². Find L, correct to the nearest mm.

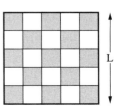

7. A square field has an area of 8 hectares. How long is each side of the field, correct to the nearest m?
[1 hectare $= 10\,000\,\text{m}^2$]

8. Here is a piece of centimetre graph paper.
Work out the area of each 'tiny' square.

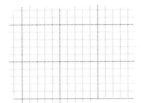

9. The area of square A is equal to the sum of the areas of squares B, C and D.
Find the length x, correct to 1 d.p.

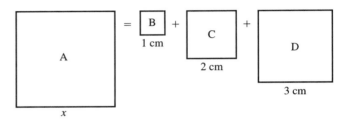

10. We know that $2^3 = 8$ ['two cubed equals 8'].

Now $\sqrt[3]{8} = 2$. The *cube root* of 8 equals 2.
The symbol $\sqrt[3]{}$ means 'the cube root of'.
Find the following
(a) $\sqrt[3]{27}$ (b) $\sqrt[3]{125}$ (c) $\sqrt[3]{1000}$ (d) $\sqrt[3]{1}$

11. A cube has a volume of $64\,\text{cm}^3$.
Find the length of the side of the cube.

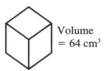

Volume
$= 64\,\text{cm}^3$

12. Solve these equations
(a) $x^2 = 9$ (b) $x^2 = 100$ (c) $x^3 = 8$
(d) $x^3 = 1000$ (e) $x^6 = 1$ (f) $x^6 = 64$

13. Use a calculator to work out $0\cdot9^n$ for $n = 2, 3, 4, 5, 6, 7, 8, 10, 20$

Copy and complete the following sentence:

'As n becomes larger and larger, $0\cdot9^n$ gets _____.'

14. Solve these equations
(a) $2^x = 8$ (b) $10^x = 100$ (c) $3^x = 81$

1.2 Written calculations

(a) *4384 + 217 + 23*

$$\begin{array}{r} 4384 \\ 217 \\ +\ \ 23 \\ \hline 4624 \\ \scriptstyle 1\ 1 \end{array}$$

(b) *472 − 235*

$$\begin{array}{r} 4\,{}^6\!7\,{}^1\!2 \\ -\ 235 \\ \hline 237 \end{array}$$

(c) *235 × 8*

$$\begin{array}{r} 235 \\ \times\ \ \ 8 \\ \hline 1880 \\ \scriptstyle 2\ 4 \end{array}$$

(d) *2·3 + 23·64*

$$\begin{array}{r} 2\cdot30 \\ +\ 23\cdot64 \\ \hline 25\cdot94 \end{array}$$ ← add zero

(e) *18 − 5·2*

$$\begin{array}{r} 1\,{}^7\!8\,\cdot\,{}^1\!0 \\ -\ \ \ \ 5\cdot2 \\ \hline 12\cdot8 \end{array}$$

(f) *0·324 × 10*

$$= 3·24$$

Move the digits one place to the left

(g) *36·7 ÷ 100*

$$= 0·367$$

Move the digits two places to the right

(h) *23 × 300*

$$= 23 × 3 × 100$$
$$= 6900$$

(i) *100·1 ÷ 7*

$$\begin{array}{r} 14\cdot3 \\ 7\overline{)10\,{}^3\!0\cdot{}^2\!1} \end{array}$$

Exercise 1

Work out, without a calculator.

1. 675 + 245
2. 6262 + 324
3. 583 − 247
4. 8417 − 5809

5. 55 × 4
6. 43 × 7
7. 324 × 5
8. 607 × 6

9. 42 × 100
10. 267 × 10
11. 15 × 1000
12. 4·21 × 10

13. 21·4 ÷ 10
14. 537 ÷ 100
15. 9·4 ÷ 10
16. 672 ÷ 100

17. Find the mystery number
    (a) a 2-digit number
        a multiple of both 3 and 4
        the sum of its digits is 15

    (b) a 3-digit number
        a square number
        the product of its digits is 2

Work out, without a calculator.

18. 34 × 20
19. 13 × 400
20. 252 × 200
21. 4983 + 3764

22. 6726 − 2918
23. 11 + 6·4
24. 12·7 − 4·5
25. 9·9 − 3·62

26. 4·3 − 2·61
27. 3 + 2·6 + 0·14
28. 264 × 7
29. 523 × 8

Exercise 2

1. Copy and complete the multiplication squares

(a)

×			9		
		54		36	
	35		15		
					48
		36	27		
7	49				

(b)

×					
	40			64	
	35	42			
			12		14
		12			
		27			63

2. Arrange in order of size, smallest first.

(a) 0·62, 0·618, 0·6   (b) 0·306, 0·4, 0·31

(c) 0·3, 0·035, 0·028   (d) 0·66, 0·166, 0·606

3. Write the number half way between:

(a) 0·3 and 0·9   (b) 0·3 and 0·4

(c) 0·1 and 0·2   (d) 0·08 and 0·09

4.

Called to account

Bordeaux: An armed robber entered a post office, brandishing a pistol and demanding Fr100,000 (£9,500). After being told the branch did not have such cash, he gave up and made a withdrawal from his own account, revealing his identity for police. He was arrested the next day. *(AFP)*

Copy and complete:

(a) £9500 = ☐ pence

(b) 1000 francs = £ ☐

(c) 95p = ☐ francs

5. Copy each sequence and fill in the spaces.

(a) 1·57, 1·58, 1·59, ☐, ☐

(b) 3·42, 3·41, 3·4, ☐, ☐

(c) ☐, 2·6, 2·8, 3, ☐

(d) ☐, 4, 4·01, 4·02, ☐

6. Work out,

(a) $204 \div 6$ (b) $434 \div 7$ (c) $7 \cdot 5 \div 3$

(d) $28 \cdot 8 \div 8$ (e) $20 \cdot 07 \div 9$ (f) $3 \cdot 6 \div 5$

7. Find the missing digits

(a)
```
     4 1 7
5) ☐ 0 ☐ 5
```

(b)
```
      2 3 7
6) ☐ 4 ☐ 2
```

(c)
```
      4 8 3
7) ☐ 3 ☐ 1
```

8. There are 85 panes of glass in each 'Geodesic' house. How many panes of glass are needed for 700 houses?

9. Work out the following

(a) $21{\cdot}7 \div 100$ (b) $285 \div 10$ (c) $37{\cdot}44 \div 6$

(d) $29{\cdot}92 \div 4$ (e) $0{\cdot}735 \div 5$ (f) $0{\cdot}938 \div 7$

10. Read the newspaper article, taken from 'The Times'.

Work out the cost of reprinting each poster.

> **No ejukashun**
> Education bosses have ordered the destruction of 50,000 posters which were distributed nationwide to promote literacy, because of spelling mistakes. They blamed proofreaders for "vocabluary" and "though" for "through". Reprints cost £8,000

Exercise 3

Copy and complete

1. (a)
```
    3 7 5
+ ☐ 4 2
  6 ☐ ☐
```

(b)
```
    6 2 0
+ ☐ 5 4
  7 ☐ 3
```

(c)
```
  ☐ 7 6
+ 3 4 ☐
  9 ☐ 9
```

2. (a)
```
    6 7 9
+ 2 ☐ 5
  ☐ 3 ☐
```

(b)
```
    3 ☐ 4
+ 4 8 9
  ☐ 7 3
```

(c)
```
    6 8 7
+ ☐ 9 ☐
  9 ☐ 3
```

3. (a)
```
      4 ☐
×     6
  2 6 4
```

(b)
```
      8 ☐
×     7
  5 8 1
```

(c)
```
  ☐ ☐ 5
×       8
  2 6 0 0
```

4. (a) ☐☐☐ $\div 7 = 35$ (b) ☐☐ $\times 13 = 182$

(c) $15 \times$ ☐ $= 120$ (d) ☐☐☐ $\div 9 = 108$

5. (a)

$$
\begin{array}{r}
7\ 4\ 6 \\
-\ 3\ 8\ \square \\
\hline
\square\ \square\ 3
\end{array}
$$

(b)

$$
\begin{array}{r}
6\ 5\ 4 \\
-\ \square\ 4\ 9 \\
\hline
2\ \square\ \square
\end{array}
$$

(c)

$$
\begin{array}{r}
8\ 6\ \square \\
-\ 4\ \square\ 5 \\
\hline
\square\ 8\ 2
\end{array}
$$

6. There is more than one correct answer for each of these questions. Ask a friend to check your solution.

(a) $\boxed{3}\ \boxed{8} - \boxed{}\boxed{} + \boxed{}\boxed{} = 37$

(b) $\boxed{4}\ \boxed{2} \times \boxed{} \div \boxed{} = 21$

(c) $\boxed{1}\ \boxed{5} \times \boxed{}\boxed{} \div \boxed{} = 45$

7. Each of these calculations has the same number missing from all three boxes. Find the missing number in each calculation.

(a) $\square \times \square - \square = 42$

(b) $\square \div \square + \square = 7$

(c) $\square \times \square + \square = 90$

8. In the circle write $+$, $-$, $\times$ or $\div$ to make the calculation correct.

(a) $8 \times 7 \bigcirc 2 = 54$ (b) $6 \times 8 \bigcirc 3 = 16$

(c) $5 \bigcirc 6 + 3 = 2$ (d) $60 \div 5 \bigcirc 8 = 20$

Multiplying decimal numbers

- When we multiply two decimal numbers together, the answer has the same number of figures after the decimal point as the total number of figures after the decimal points in the question.

(a) 0.2×0.6
$(2 \times 6 = 12)$
So $0.2 \times 0.6 = 0.12$

(b) 0.3×0.05
$(3 \times 5 = 15)$
So $0.3 \times 0.05 = 0.015$

Exercise 4

1. 6×0.3 **2.** 8×0.2 **3.** 7×0.4 **4.** 12×0.3

5. 0.5×3 **6.** 0.3×0.2 **7.** 0.5×0.1 **8.** 7×0.22

9. 15×0.3 **10.** 0.6×0.02 **11.** 0.01×18 **12.** 22×0.03

13. 0.31×0.8 **14.** 17×0.03 **15.** 28×0.2 **16.** 15.2×0.2

17. 4.03×0.4 **18.** 20.7×0.4 **19.** 0.3^2 **20.** 0.01^2

Dividing by a decimal number

To divide by a decimal number we transform the calculation into a division by a *whole number*.

Examples $4.8 \div 0.4 = 48 \div 4 = 12$ [Multiply 4·8 and 0·4 by 10]

                 $5.4 \div 0.06 = 540 \div 6 = 90$ [Multiply 5·4 and 0·06 by 100]

                 $0.8 \div 0.02 = 80 \div 2 = 40$ [Multiply 0·8 and 0·02 by 100]

Since both numbers are multiplied by 10 or 100, the answer is not changed.

Exercise 5

Work out, without a calculator

1. $2.48 \div 0.2$
2. $2.92 \div 0.4$
3. $0.63 \div 0.3$
4. $0.528 \div 0.1$
5. $1.72 \div 0.1$
6. $0.875 \div 0.5$
7. $0.522 \div 0.6$
8. $8.28 \div 0.2$
9. $5.04 \div 0.7$
10. $0.36 \div 0.02$
11. $0.95 \div 0.05$
12. $1.44 \div 0.04$
13. $100 \div 0.1$
14. $0.8 \div 0.5$
15. $0.7 \div 0.4$
16. $0.39 \div 0.006$
17. $0.936 \div 0.03$
18. $0.5111 \div 0.001$
19. $0.48 \div 0.24$
20. $0.7 \div 0.35$
21. $17.4 \div 0.2$
22. $54 \div 0.3$
23. $0.2 \div 0.2$
24. $0.7 \div 0.07$

Copy and complete these operator squares. The arrows act as equals signs.

25.

8	÷		→	
×		−		
	÷	0·05	→	
↓		↓		
	−	0·15	→	0·65

26.

20	×	0·6	→	
÷		×		
0·1	×		→	1
↓		↓		
	×		→	

27.

15	×		→	4·5
÷		×		
	÷		→	
↓		↓		
300	×	0·03	→	

Exercise Pudding

Pudding buyer can fly free for a lifetime

DAVID PHILLIPS went on a massive shopping spree and California's so-called "Pudding Guy" won free airline travel for life.

Mr Phillips spotted the special offer in the frozen-food aisle of his local supermarket.

The promotion by Healthy Choice foods promised 500 frequent flier miles for every ten bar codes from its products sent in by

the end of the year. "Early birds" who sent in bar codes by May 31 would get double credit: 1,000 free miles.

Mr Phillips set out on a shopping spree that ultimately earned him 1.25 million frequent flier miles, for just $3,140. "I quickly did the maths and realised what this could mean," he told our reporter.

At first he sought out Healthy Choice soups, but

soon found a "goldmine" in the form of a discount supermarket chain that sold Healthy Choice chocolate puddings for just 25 cents each.

He and his mother-in-law raided all ten local branches for the Healthy Choice puddings, even asking one shop manager to order an extra 60 cases for him. By the time he was done, he had bought ☐ cups of pudding.

Read the newspaper article above.   [$1 = 100 cents]

1. Assume that Mr Phillips bought all his chocolate puddings at the discount price of 25 cents each. How many did he buy?

2. From London to New York is about 5500 miles. How many times could Mr Phillips fly on that route?

Mixed questions

Exercise 6

State whether the following are 'True' or 'False'.

1. $4 \cdot 2 \times 1000 = 4200$
2. $0 \cdot 61 \times 100 = 0 \cdot 6100$
3. $5 + 8 \cdot 9 = 13 \cdot 9$
4. $7 \cdot 44 \div 6 = 1 \cdot 24$
5. $13 \cdot 6 + 3 = 13 \cdot 9$
6. $0 \cdot 844 \div 10 = 8 \cdot 44$
7. $7 \cdot 41 - 1 \cdot 9 = 5 \cdot 51$
8. $4 \cdot 2 \times 50 = 210$
9. $7 - 3 \cdot 64 = 3 \cdot 36$
10. $8 \div 100 = 0 \cdot 8$
11. $1 \cdot 41 + 13 \cdot 5 = 14 \cdot 91$
12. $8 \cdot 75 + 19 = 26 \cdot 75$
13. $2 \cdot 14 \times 1000 = 2140$
14. $4 - 0 \cdot 65 = 3 \cdot 35$
15. $25 \cdot 6 \div 50 = 0 \cdot 512$

Work out the following.

16. £5 − £4·12
17. £10 − £7·34
18. £7 − £2·45
19. $4 \cdot 2 \div 0 \cdot 2$
20. $1 \cdot 944 \div 0 \cdot 6$
21. $6 \cdot 9 \div 0 \cdot 05$
22. $3 \cdot 6 \times 10 \times 100$
23. $4 \cdot 5 \times 0 \cdot 1 \times 1000$
24. $0 \cdot 007 \times 10$
25. $11 - 2 \cdot 95$
26. $1 \cdot 2 + 14$
27. $0 \cdot 014\,56 \div 0 \cdot 04$
28. $0 \cdot 1 \div 100$
29. $45 \cdot 7 \times 0 \cdot 07$
30. $6 \cdot 279 \div 0 \cdot 7$

Exercise 7

(a) Start in the top left box.
(b) Work out the answer to the calculation in the box.
(c) Find the answer in the top corner of another box.
(d) Write down the letter in that box.
(e) Repeat steps (b), (c) and (d) until you arrive back at the top left box. What is the message?

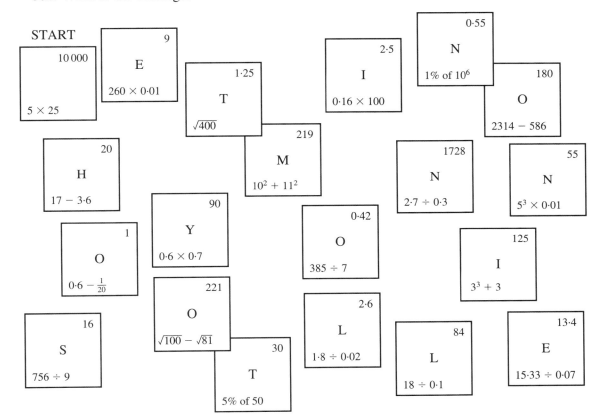

Long multiplication

● Seventeen 25s is the same as ten 25s plus seven 25s
  17×25 is the same as $10 \times 25 + 7 \times 25$

(a) $\begin{array}{r} 25 \\ \times\ 10 \\ \hline 250 \end{array}$ (b) $\begin{array}{r} 25 \\ \times\ 7 \\ \hline 175 \end{array}$ (c) $\begin{array}{r} 250 \\ +\ 175 \\ \hline 425 \end{array}$ (d) Answer: 425

● $26 \times 35 = 20 \times 35 + 6 \times 35$

(a) $\begin{array}{r} 35 \\ \times\ 20 \\ \hline 700 \end{array}$ (b) $\begin{array}{r} 35 \\ \times\ 6 \\ \hline 210 \\ \scriptstyle 3 \end{array}$ (c) $\begin{array}{r} 700 \\ +\ 210 \\ \hline 910 \end{array}$ (d) Answer: 910

14

Exercise 8

Work out

1. 15×23 2. 14×31 3. 16×32 4. 17×14

5. 18×33 6. 19×24 7. 17×31 8. 13×52

9. 14×42 10. 13×27 11. 15×22 12. 16×19

13. 12×47 14. 18×51 15. 19×62 16. 17×46

17. 15×56 18. 14×81 19. 18×29 20. 13×73

Long multiplication using grids

Here is a different method for long multiplication. It is highly recommended so give it a try, especially if you find the 'ordinary method' difficult.

- We write numbers in grids, for example:

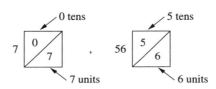

- Watch carefully for 23×7. Write 23 above the grid and 7 on the right

- Multiply the digits separately. Write the answer in its box.

- Add along each diagonal and write the answer at the end. Work from right to left So $23 \times 7 = 161$

- Here are two more examples

52×17
$= 884$

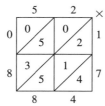

734×23
$= 16\,882$

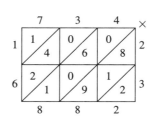

15

Exercise 9

Work out

1.

2.

3.
```
  2   5
 ┌──┬──┐
 │╱ │╱ │ 7
 └──┴──┘
```

4.
```
  3   1
 ┌──┬──┐
 │╱ │╱ │ 8
 └──┴──┘
```

5.

6.
```
  3   5
 ┌──┬──┐
 │╱ │╱ │ 1
 ├──┼──┤
 │╱ │╱ │ 5
 └──┴──┘
```

7. 21 × 24   **8.** 27 × 32   **9.** 26 × 28   **10.** 27 × 21

11. 32 × 25   **12.** 33 × 27   **13.** 36 × 14   **14.** 35 × 27

15. 34 × 41   **16.** 42 × 61   **17.** 31 × 47   **18.** 53 × 21

19. 123 × 32   **20.** 291 × 42   **21.** 804 × 61   **22.** 74 × 243

23. 62 × 831   **24.** 53 × 747   **25.** 249 × 92   **26.** 603 × 27

27. 231 × 314   **28.** 411 × 306   **29.** 4124 × 314   **30.** 6036 × 147

Long division

A Use the method for 'short division' with working at the side.

$$16\overline{)4\,0^81}$$
$$\quad 2\,5 \text{ remainder } 1$$

$$
\begin{array}{r}
16 \\
\times\ 2 \\
\hline
32 \\
\end{array}
$$

$$
\begin{array}{r}
16 \\
\times\ 5 \\
\hline
80 \\
\end{array}
$$

B In this method we set it out so that the remainders are easier to find

$$
\begin{array}{r}
25 \\
16\overline{)401} \\
-\ 32\downarrow \\
\hline
81 \\
-\ 80 \\
\hline
1 \\
\end{array}
$$

- 16 into 40 goes 2 times
- 2 × 16 = 32
- 40 − 32 = 8
- 'bring down' 1
- 16 into 81 goes 5 times
- 5 × 16 = 80
- 81 − 80 = 1
- Answer is 25 remainder 1

Exercise 10

1. 13)288   **2.** 13)416   **3.** 16)384   **4.** 17)442

5. 16)496   **6.** 15)495   **7.** 19)665   **8.** 21)777

9. 17)697   **10.** 15)516   **11.** 14)672   **12.** 17)550

13. 500 ÷ 22   **14.** 840 ÷ 24   **15.** 598 ÷ 23   **16.** 752 ÷ 26

17. 317 ÷ 31   **18.** 547 ÷ 25   **19.** 886 ÷ 42   **20.** 963 ÷ 33

16

21. $557 \div 26$	**22.** $528 \div 45$	**23.** $118 \div 52$	**24.** $785 \div 63$
25. $32)\overline{715}$	**26.** $18)\overline{924}$	**27.** $25)\overline{776}$	**28.** $53)\overline{781}$
29. $64)\overline{696}$	**30.** $27)\overline{583}$	**31.** $15)\overline{667}$	**32.** $98)\overline{694}$

Word problems

A minibus can take 16 passengers. How many minibuses are needed for 214 passengers?

(a) Work out $214 \div 16$

```
      13 remainder 6
  16)214
      16
      54
      48
       6
```

(b) You have to think carefully about what the remainder means. If you used 13 minibuses there would be 6 people left over. So you need 14 minibuses altogether.

Exercise 11

To do these questions you have to multiply or divide. Do not use a calculator.

1. Work out the total cost of 35 drinks at 32p each. Give your answer in pounds.

2. A box of 24 tins costs 864 pence. How much does each tin cost?

3. There are 34 rooms in a school and each room has 28 chairs. How many chairs are there altogether?

4. Read the newspaper article shown. Each leech requires 35 mg of blood. How much blood is needed for a dozen leeches?

5. Eggs are packed twelve to a box. How many boxes are needed for 444 eggs?

6. How many 52-seater coaches will be needed for a school trip for a party of 354?

Blood lust satisfied

Hungry new arrivals at a zoo were saved when the staff became blood donors. A dozen leeches delivered to Drusillas in Alfriston, East Sussex, were craving fresh blood and the only way to satisfy them was to attach them to workers who volunteered to help. Gemma Walker, 25, an education worker at the zoo, said: "I was quite surprised at how quickly it attached itself. It drilled its head into my arm and as its teeth went in it felt a bit like being stung with nettles. I was told it would probably feed for about ten minutes but it kept going for well over an hour. It grew to about three times its size and then fell off." The leeches need feeding every two months or so, preferably on human blood.

7. It costs £4275 to hire a plane for a day. A trip is organised for 45 people. How much does each person pay?

8. Tins of dog food are packed 36 to a box. How many boxes are needed for 800 tins?

9. A prize of 1000 Easter eggs is shared equally between 15 winners. How many eggs does each winner get and how many are left over?

Questions with decimals

(a) 3.14×1.3

- Ignore the decimals.
  Work out

$$
\begin{array}{r}
314 \\
\times\ 13 \\
\hline
3140 \\
942 \\
\hline
4082
\end{array}
$$

- There are three figures after the decimal points in the numbers being multiplied. So there are three figures after the point in the answer.

$3.14 \times 1.3 = 4.082$

(b) $1.8 \div 0.025$

- Multiply both numbers by 1000 so that you can divide by a whole number.

So work out $1800 \div 25$

$$
\begin{array}{r}
72 \\
25)\overline{1800} \\
175 \\
\hline
50 \\
50 \\
\hline
0
\end{array}
$$

Exercise 12

Work out.

1. 4.5×2.1
2. 8.6×4.1
3. 7.3×0.2
4. 3.7×1.8

5. 11.5×0.8
6. 8.4×0.13
7. 14.2×0.7
8. 6.9×4.2

9. 1.51×0.22
10. 4.6×82
11. 0.73×37
12. 0.33×1.24

13. $8 \div 0.5$
14. $1.32 \div 0.12$
15. $1.08 \div 0.9$
16. $1.25 \div 0.5$

17. $3.38 \div 1.3$
18. $24 \div 1.2$
19. $0.638 \div 0.05$
20. $4.44 \div 0.08$

21. $67.8 \div 0.024$
22. $1.612 \div 0.31$
23. $3.944 \div 1.7$
24. $1.088 \div 0.32$

1.3 Rules of algebra

Using letters for numbers

Many problems in mathematics are easier to solve when algebra is used. When letters like x, y, a or n are used in the working of a question, it is important to remember that the *letters stand for numbers*.

(a) Suppose I start with the number 7, add 6 and then divide the result by 100.

The number I have at the end is $\dfrac{7+6}{100}$, which is $\dfrac{13}{100}$.

(b) Suppose I start with the number x, add 5 and then divide the result by z.

The expression I have at the end is $\dfrac{x+5}{z}$.

(c) Start with n, multiply by 7 and then add 3. $n \rightarrow 7n \rightarrow 7n + 3$

(d) Start with m, subtract 5 and then multiply the result by 2. $m \rightarrow m - 5 \rightarrow 2(m - 5)$

(e) Start with a, add h and then square the result. $a \rightarrow a + h \rightarrow (a + h)^2$

(f) Suppose one pistol weighs 600 grams.
Then x pistols weigh $600x$ grams
[Remember $600x$ means '$600 \times x$'.]

(g) Suppose a prize of £n is shared equally between y people.

Each person receives £$\dfrac{n}{y}$.

Exercise 1

In Questions **1** to **12** write down the expression you are left with after following the instructions. If any of your answers contain brackets, do not remove them.

1. Start with x, double it and then add 5.

2. Start with y, subtract 7 and then multiply the result by 3.

3. Start with y, treble it and then subtract 8.

4. Start with n, double it, subtract 7, and then multiply the result by 4.

5. Start with x, multiply by 4 and then take the result *away from* 12.

6. Start with a, multiply by 7, take the result away from 10 and then multiply the result by 3.

7. Start with h, subtract t and then multiply the result by 5.

8. Start with p, add 5 and then multiply the result by d.

9. Start with a, double it and then add A.

10. Start with n, multiply by k, subtract u and then add b.

11. Start with e, subtract u, add h and then multiply the result by k.

12. Start with x, subtract t, add y and then divide the result by u.

13. A model of Stonehenge consists of n stones. How many stones are there in three such models? How many stones are there in x models?

14. A small bag of peanuts contains y nuts, and a large bag contains 3 times as many. If a boy buys a large bag and then eats 10 nuts, how many are left in his bag?

15. A basketball player scored x points in each of his first three games and then he scored y points in each of his next two games. How many points did he score altogether?

16. Bill used to earn £n per week. He then had a rise of £r per week. How much will he now earn in 10 weeks?

17. In a shop: tapes cost £t each;
C.D.s cost £c each;
records cost £r each.

Write down the total cost of
(a) 3 tapes and 1 C.D.   (b) 1 record, 5 tapes and 2 C.D.s

(c) m tapes and 3 C.D.s   (d) p records and 5 tapes

Simplifying terms

Simplify the following expressions.

$3n \times 2 = 6n$ $2m \times 10 = 20m$

$10a \div 2 = 5a$ $8R \div 4 = 2R$

$m \times m = m^2$ $2a \times a = 2a^2$

$3n \times 2n = 6n^2$ $4t \times 5t = 20t$

Exercise 2

Do the following multiplications and divisions.

1. $3x \times 4$ **2.** $2x \times 5$ **3.** $7x \times 2$

4. $6y \times 2$ **5.** $3y \times 5$ **6.** $4a \times 6$

7. $6a \times 10$ **8.** $3c \times 9$ **9.** $4d \times 6$

10. $7 \times 2c$ **11.** $5 \times 4d$ **12.** $4 \times 3t$

13. $8 \times 2a$ **14.** $11 \times 3d$ **15.** $9 \times 2x$

16. $16b \div 4$ **17.** $32x \div 8$ **18.** $2T \div 2$

19. $44h \div 11$ **20.** $15R \div 5$ **21.** $9t \div 9$

22. $30n \div 6$ **23.** $6A \div 3$ **24.** $7M \div 7$

25. $24r \div 6$ **26.** $80t \div 8$ **27.** $36T \div 4$

28. $25a \div 5$ **29.** $90R \div 10$ **30.** $9b \div 3$

31. $n \times n$ **32.** $a \times a$ **33.** $T \times T$

34. $2c \times c$ **35.** $2n \times n$ **36.** $3b \times b$

37. $y \times 2y$ **38.** $A \times A$ **39.** $t \times 4t$

40. $n \times 5n$ **41.** $2x \times 3x$ **42.** $3c \times 4c$

43. $4a \times 2a$ **44.** $3t \times 3t$ **45.** $2n \times 3n$

Simplify the following expressions.

(a) $3(2n + 5) = 6n + 15$

(b) $2(5a - 3) = 10a - 6$

(c) $-3(2x - 7) = -6x + 21$

(d) $3(3n + 1) + 2n = 9n + 3 + 2n$
$= 11n + 3$

(e) $4(a + 2) + 3(2a + 1)$
$= 4a + 8 + 6a + 3$
$= 10a + 11$

Exercise 3

Remove the brackets from the following expressions.

1. $2(3x + 4)$ **2.** $5(5y - 2)$

3. $10(2x - 1)$ **4.** $3(2x + 5y)$

5. $4(7y + 2)$ **6.** $6(2a + 3)$

7. $7(10 - 3x)$ **8.** $5(2y - 5)$

9. $3(4a - 5)$ **10.** $2(3y + 1)$

11. $7(2a + 9)$ **12.** $8(3y - 5)$

13. $5(12c - 1)$ **14.** $9(3d - 4)$

15. $-2(x + 5)$ **16.** $-4(y - 3)$

17. $-3(a - 1)$ **18.** $3(t + 4)$

19. $-2(x + 3)$ **20.** $4(y - 2)$

21. $10(b - 3)$ **22.** $-5(c + 10)$

23. $-6(d + h)$ **24.** $2(x + y)$

25. $7(a + 2b)$ **26.** $-2(2x - y)$

27. $-3(5a - 3)$ **28.** $4(2a - 1)$

Exercise 4

Simplify the following expressions.

1. $3(x + 2) + 4x$

2. $5(2y - 1) - 3y$

3. $2(4x + 1) - 7$

4. $4(2n + 1) + 2(n - 1)$

5. $5(a + 2) + 2(2a + 1)$

6. $3(t - 1) + 2(2t + 1)$

7. $2(4x + 3) + 4(3x - 4)$

8. $3(4d + 1) - 2(6d - 5)$

9. $5a + 2(3a + 4) - 2a$

10. $9y - 5(y + 2) - 3$

11. $11b + 3 - 3(2b - 5)$

12. $4(a - 2) + 2(3a - 1) - 3a$

13. $5(3x - 2) - 4 - 2(4 + x)$

14. $2c + 5(c - 2) - 3(2c + 3)$

15. $6y + 2(3y + 1) - 7 + 2y$

16. $5 - 3(2x + 3) + 4(5x + 3)$

17. $20 - 3(a + 3) - 4(2a - 1)$

18. $9(x + 2) - 4 + 3(2 - 3x)$

19. $15(n + m) - 6(2n - m)$

20. $8(a - b) + 10(a - 3b)$

Exercise 5

In Questions **1** to **15** answer 'true' or 'false'.

1. $3 \times n = n \times 3$ **2.** $5 \times a = 5 + a$ **3.** $n \times n = n^2$

4. $c \times d = cd$ **5.** $m \times 3 = 3m$ **6.** $a - b = b - a$

7. $2(n + 1) = 2n + 1$ **8.** $t + t = t^2$ **9.** $2h \times h = 2h^2$

10. $m \times 3m = 3m^2$ **11.** $3(a - b) = 3a - 3b$ **12.** $n^2 + n^2 = n^4$

13. $n \div 3 = \dfrac{n}{3}$ **14.** $t \div 2 = \dfrac{t}{2}$ **15.** $(x + y) \div 2 = \dfrac{(x + y)}{2}$

16. In the expression $2(3n - 5)$, three operations are performed in the following order:

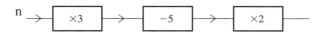

Draw similar diagrams to show the correct order of operations for the following expressions.

(a) $6n + 1$ (b) $3(5n - 2)$ (c) $\dfrac{4n + 5}{3}$

(d) $n^2 + 7$ (e) $(n - 7)^2$ (f) $\dfrac{(3n + 1)^2 + 5}{7}$

Remove the brackets and simplify

(a) $n(n + 2)$ (b) $x(2x + 1)$ (c) $a(3a - 2)$
    $= n^2 + 2n$ $= 2x^2 + x$ $= 3a^2 - 2a$

(d) $2m(m + 1)$ (e) $5n(2n + 3)$ (f) $2n(3n + 1)$
    $= 2m^2 + 2m$ $= 10n^2 + 15n$ $= 6n^2 + 2n$

Exercise 6

Remove the brackets and simplify.

1. $n(n + 3)$ **2.** $n(n + 7)$ **3.** $a(a - 3)$

4. $t(t - 5)$ **5.** $a(a - 10)$ **6.** $m(m + 11)$

7. $2a(a + 1)$ **8.** $3n(n + 2)$ **9.** $5t(t + 1)$

10. $x(2x + 1)$ **11.** $y(y - 7)$ **12.** $3y(y + 3)$

13. $h(h - 100)$ **14.** $5a(a + 5)$ **15.** $p(p + 3)$

16. $2e(3e + 1)$ **17.** $3x(3x + 2)$ **18.** $2a(5a - 1)$

22

Exercise 7

1. Four rods P, Q, R and S have lengths, in cm, as shown.

In each diagram find the length l, in terms of x. Give your answers in their simplest form. [The diagrams are not drawn to scale.]

(a)

(b)

(c)

(d)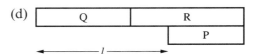

(e)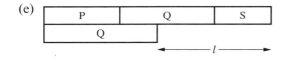

(f)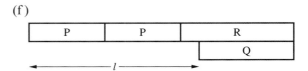

(g)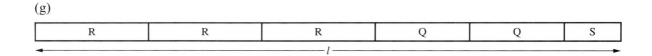

(h)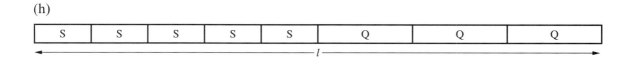

(i)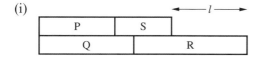

(j)

(k)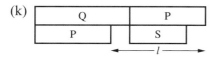

(l)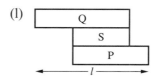

Factors

- The expression $8x + 6$ has two terms, $8x$ and 6.
  The number 2 is a factor of both terms.
  We can write $8x + 6 = 2(4x + 3)$.
  This process is called factorising.

- Here are some examples:
  $6a + 15 = 3(2a + 5)$ $18m + 24n = 6(3m + 4n)$
  $4x^2 + 6x = 2x(2x + 3)$ $7n^2 + 5n = n(7n + 5)$

Exercise 8

Copy and complete.

1. $8a + 10 = 2(4a + \square)$
2. $6x + 3 = 3(2x + \square)$
3. $6a + 9 = 3(2a + \square)$
4. $10a + 15 = 5(\square + \square)$
5. $18x - 12 = 6(\square - \square)$
6. $18c + 24 = \square(\square + \square)$
7. $3x + 15 = \square(\square + \square)$
8. $7n - 35 = 7(\square - \square)$
9. $16m + 40 = \square(2m + \square)$
10. $45a + 36 = \square(5a + \square)$

In Questions **11** to **25** factorise the expressions.

11. $4a + 10$
12. $6c + 21$
13. $10c - 5$
14. $18m + 9$
15. $9m + 12$
16. $15a + 25$
17. $14x - 21t$
18. $18x + 24t$
19. $24p - 20q$
20. $6a + 9b + 3c$
21. $10a + 15b + 25c$
22. $9x + 9y + 21t$
23. $7c + 14d - 7e$
24. $24m + 12n + 16t$
25. $18a - 27b + 36c$

Factorise the following.

26. $x^2 + 6x$
27. $3x^2 + 4x$
28. $6x^2 + x$
29. $2a^2 + a$
30. $5n^2 + n$
31. $2a^2 + 6a$
32. $3n^2 - n$
33. $5m^2 - 15m$
34. $x^3 + x^2 + x$
35. $12a^2 - 8a$
36. $6a^2 - a$
37. $mn + m^2$
38. $x^2 - xy$
39. $2x^2 + 4xy$
40. $x^3 + xy^2$

1.4 Circles

Circumference

- The perimeter of a circle is called *circumference*

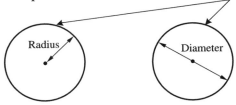

- The distance from the centre of a circle to the circumference is called *radius*

- The distance across a circle through its centre is called *diameter*

- The diameter is twice the radius. If we write *d* for diameter and *r* for radius then $d = 2r$

Exercise 1 [oral]

Find the radius and the diameter of each circle.

1.

32 mm

2.

26 cm

3.

7 m

4.
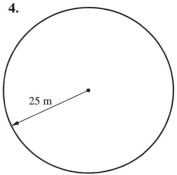
25 m

5.

22 mm

6.
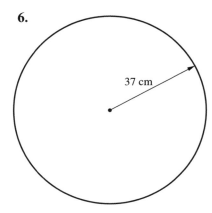
37 cm

22 cm

A piece of string 22 cm long will make:

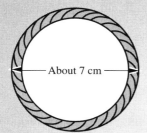

About 7 cm

A circle whose diameter is just over 7 cm.

If you divide the circumference of a circle by its diameter the number you obtain is always just over three.

$$\frac{\text{circumference}}{\text{diameter}} \approx 3$$

which means

$$\boxed{\text{Circumference} \approx 3 \times \text{diameter}}$$

This provides a fairly good *estimate* for the circumference of any circle.

Exercise 2

Estimate the circumference of each circle

1.
7 cm

2.
17 mm

3.
5 m

4.
26 mm

5.
12 mm

6.
2 cm

7.
15 cm

8.
40 cm

9.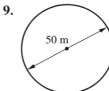
50 m

Pi

- For any circle, the exact value of the ratio $\left(\dfrac{\text{circumference}}{\text{diameter}}\right)$ is a number denoted by the Greek letter π.

  Since $\dfrac{c}{d} = \pi$, we can write $\boxed{c = \pi \times d}$. Learn this formula.

  Most calculators have a $\boxed{\pi}$ button, which will give the value of π correct to at least 6 decimal places: $3{\cdot}141593$.

- The number π has fascinated mathematicians for thousands of years. The Egyptians had a value of $3{\cdot}16$ in 1500 B.C. In about 250 B.C. the Greek mathematician Archimedes showed that π was between $3\frac{10}{71}$ and $3\frac{10}{70}$. He considered regular polygons with many sides. As the number of sides in the polygon increased, so the polygon became nearer and nearer to a circle.

  Ludolph Van Ceulen (1540–1610) obtained a value of π correct to 35 significant figures. He was so proud of his work that he had the number engraved on his tombstone.

'Lovely sunny Greece, home of Pi'

Exercise 3

Make a table and complete it for Questions **1** to **12**. Make sure you write the correct units.

Number	Radius r	Diameter d	Estimated circumference	Calculated circumference
1	2 cm			
2				

1. 2 cm

2. 5 cm

3. 9 m

4. 30 mm

5. 8 km

6. 20 m

7. 25 m

8. 23 mm

9. 50 cm

10. 37 m

11. 68 km

12. 10 mm

A circular tin of diameter 9 cm rolls along the
floor for a distance of 3 m. How many times
does it rotate completely?

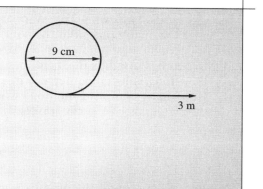

circumference $= \pi \times 9$
$= 28 \cdot 274334$ cm
3 m $= 300$ cm

Number of rotations $= \dfrac{300}{28 \cdot 274334}$

$= 10 \cdot 61$

The tin makes 10 *complete* rotations.

Exercise 4

Give your answers correct to 1 d.p. unless told otherwise.

1. The tip of the minute hand of a clock is 8 cm
from the centre of the clock face. Calculate
the distance moved by the tip of the minute
hand in one hour.

2. A bicycle wheel of diameter 80 cm makes 20 complete rotations
as the bicycle moves forward in a straight line. Find the
circumference of the wheel and work out how far the bicycle
moves forward. Give your answers in metres.

3. A tennis ball of diameter 7 cm rolls in a straight line so that it
makes 10 complete revolutions. How far does it roll? Give your
answer to the nearest cm.

4. Which has the longer perimeter and by how much: an equilateral
triangle of side 10 cm or a circle of diameter 10 cm?

5. A tin of tomatoes has diameter 7·5 cm. The tin is wrapped in a
paper cover which is long enough to allow 1 cm overlap for
fixing. How long is the cover?

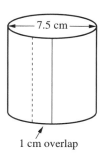

6. The wheels on Gill's bike have a diameter of 62 cm. Gill rolls
forward a distance of 1200 cm. Calculate how many times the
wheels go round *completely*.

7. In a coin rolling competition Gemma rolls a one pound coin on its edge a distance of 4·2 m. A one pound coin has diameter 2·2 cm. How many times did the coin rotate completely?

8. A car tyre has a radius of 37 cm.
   (a) How long is its circumference in cm?
   (b) How many complete rotations will the tyre make if the car travels 2 km?

9. A newt walks around the edge of a circular pond at a speed of 2 cm/s. How long will it take to walk all the way round if the radius of the pond is 1·3 m?

10. A trundle wheel can be used for measuring distances along roads or pavements. A wheel of circumference one metre is pushed along and distance is measured by counting the number of rotations of the wheel. Calculate the diameter of the wheel to the nearest mm.

11. The perimeter of a circular pond is 11·7 m. Calculate the diameter of the pond to the nearest cm.

12. The tip of the minute hand of Big Ben is 4·6 m from the centre of the clock face. Calculate the distance, in km, moved by the end of the minute hand in one year (365 days).

Perimeters

Calculate the perimeter of the shape.

The perimeter consists of a semi-circle and 3 straight lines.

Length of semi-circle $= \dfrac{\pi \times 10}{2}$

$= \pi \times 5 \text{ cm}$

$\therefore$ Perimeter of shape $= (\pi \times 5) + 4 + 10 + 4$

$= 33 \cdot 7 \text{ cm (to 1 d.p.)}$

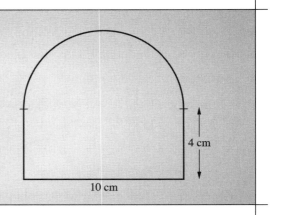

4 cm

10 cm

Exercise 5

Calculate the perimeter of each shape. All arcs are either semi-circles or quarter circles. Give answers correct to 1 d.p.

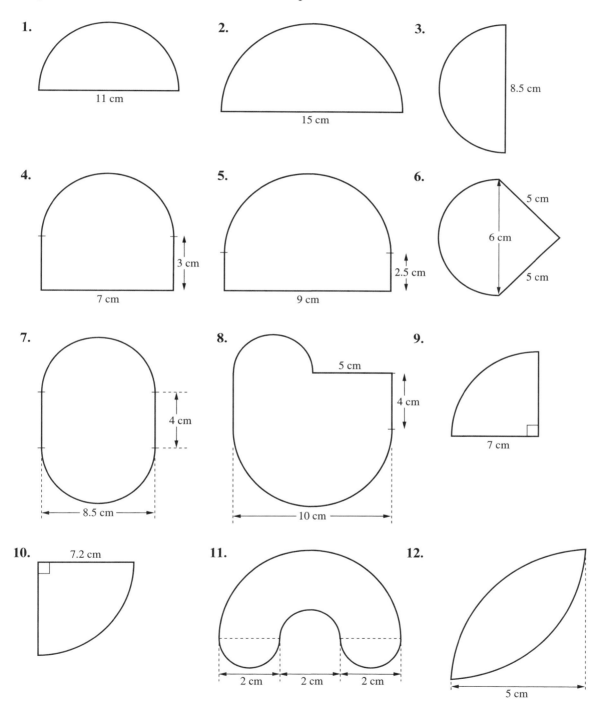

1.

11 cm

2.

15 cm

3.

8.5 cm

4.

3 cm

7 cm

5.

2.5 cm

9 cm

6.

5 cm

6 cm

5 cm

7.

4 cm

8.5 cm

8.

5 cm

4 cm

10 cm

9.

4 cm

7 cm

10.

7.2 cm

11.

2 cm   2 cm   2 cm

12.

5 cm

Area of a circle

(a) The circle below is divided into 12 equal sectors

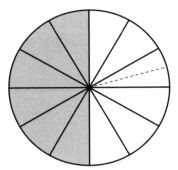

(b) The sectors are cut and arranged to make a shape which is nearly a rectangle. (one sector is cut in half).

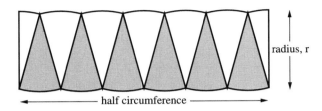

radius, r

half circumference

(c) The approximate area can be found as follows:

length of rectangle ≈ half circumference of circle

$$\approx \frac{\pi \times 2r}{2}$$

$$\approx \pi r$$

width of rectangle ≈ r

∴ area of rectangle ≈ $\pi r \times r$

$$\approx \pi r^2$$

If larger and larger numbers of sectors were used, this approximation would become more and more accurate.

This is a demonstration of an important result.

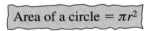

Area of a circle = πr^2 *Learn* this formula.

Note: πr^2 means $\pi(r^2)$.

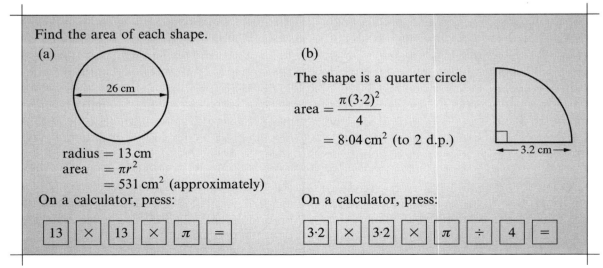

Find the area of each shape.

(a)

26 cm

radius = 13 cm
area   = πr^2
       = 531 cm² (approximately)
On a calculator, press:

| 13 | × | 13 | × | π | = |

(b)

The shape is a quarter circle

$$\text{area} = \frac{\pi(3.2)^2}{4}$$

$$= 8.04 \, \text{cm}^2 \text{ (to 2 d.p.)}$$

3.2 cm

On a calculator, press:

| 3·2 | × | 3·2 | × | π | ÷ | 4 | = |

Exercise 6

In Questions **1** to **8** calculate the area of each circle correct to 1 d.p.

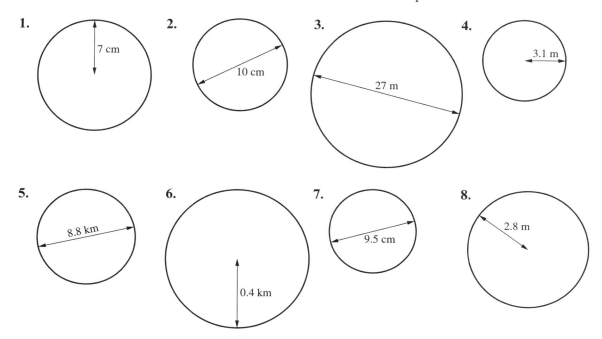

1. 7 cm

2. 10 cm

3. 27 m

4. 3.1 m

5. 8.8 km

6. 0.4 km

7. 9.5 cm

8. 2.8 m

9. When hunting for food, an eagle flies over a circular region of radius 3·5 km. What is the area of this region in km²?

10. A carton of 'Verdone' weedkiller contains enough weedkiller to treat an area of 100 m². A circular lawn at Hampton Court has a radius of 16·5 m. How many cartons of weedkiller are needed to treat this lawn?

In Questions **11** to **14** find the area of each shape. All arcs are either semi-circles or quarter circles and the units are cm.

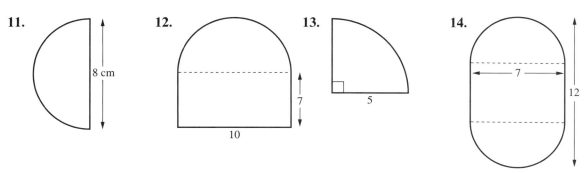

11. 8 cm

12. 7, 10

13. 5

14. 7, 12

In Questions **15** to **20** find the shaded area. Lengths are in cm.

15.

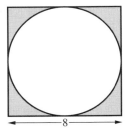

16.

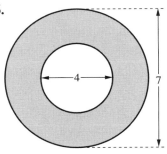

17.

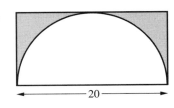

18.

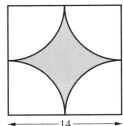

19.

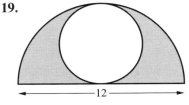

20.

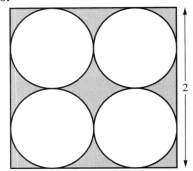

21. An old fashioned telephone dial has the dimensions shown. The diameter of each finger hole is 1 cm.
Calculate the shaded area.

22. A circular pond of radius 3·6 m is surrounded by a concrete path 70 cm wide.
Calculate the area of the surface of the path.

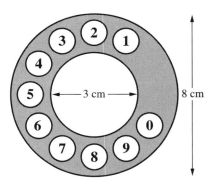

23.

Hamster's friction burns

A house fire that caused almost £400 in damages has been blamed on a hamster trundling its treadmill so fast that the friction caused sparks that set fire to the bedding in its cage. The explanation has been accepted by loss adjusters investigating the fire at the home of Steve Lewis, a chef, and his wife, Dawn, in Clayton, Newcastle-under-Lyme. When the smoke alarm went off, Mr Lewis found the hamster's cage, lounge curtains and carpets ablaze. He rescued the pet, which escaped with singed ears and whiskers.

The diameter of a treadmill is 10 cm. At full speed the hamster makes it rotate 5 times in one second. How 'far' does the hamster run in one second?

1.5 Fractions

As you progress further in mathematics, the ability to handle fractions with confidence becomes more and more important. Mistakes are frequently made when algebraic expressions contain fractions.

Fractions involving algebraic symbols can be manipulated in the same way as ordinary numerical fractions. This section begins with a discussion of arithmetic with fractions.

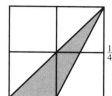

Multiplying

(a) $\frac{3}{4}$ of $12 = \frac{3}{4} \times \frac{12}{1}$

$= \frac{36}{4}$

$= 9$

(b) $\frac{2}{3} \times \frac{5}{7} = \frac{10}{21}$

(c) $2\frac{1}{2} \times \frac{1}{4} = \frac{5}{2} \times \frac{1}{4}$

$= \frac{5}{8}$

Method: (i) Write any mixed fractions as top heavy fractions.
(ii) Multiply the numbers on the top
(iii) Multiply the numbers on the bottom.
(iv) Cancel down if necessary. This can be done either before or after multiplying.

[Example (a) could be $\dfrac{3}{\underset{1}{\cancel{4}}} \times \dfrac{\overset{3}{\cancel{12}}}{1} = \dfrac{9}{1} = 9$]

Dividing

(a) How many quarters are there in 3?

There are four quarters in one, so there are 12 quarters in 3. That is $3 \div \frac{1}{4} = 12$.

(b) Similarly we find that $3 \div \frac{1}{5} = 15$

and $8 \div \frac{1}{3} = 24$

Method: (i) Invert the fraction you are dividing by and then multiply the two fractions.
(ii) Write any mixed fractions as top heavy fractions.

Examples:

$\frac{3}{5} \div \frac{2}{3}$

$= \frac{3}{5} \times \frac{3}{2}$

$= \frac{9}{10}$

$\frac{8}{15} \div \frac{4}{5}$

$= \dfrac{\overset{2}{\cancel{8}}}{\underset{3}{\cancel{15}}} \times \dfrac{\overset{1}{\cancel{5}}}{\underset{1}{\cancel{4}}}$

$= \frac{2}{3}$

$2\frac{1}{3} \div \frac{3}{4}$

$= \frac{7}{3} \times \frac{4}{3}$

$= \frac{28}{9}$

$= 3\frac{1}{9}$

Exercise 1

1. Work out

(a) $\frac{2}{3} \times \frac{1}{5}$ (b) $\frac{3}{5} \times \frac{3}{4}$ (c) $\frac{5}{7} \times \frac{3}{4}$ (d) $\frac{2}{5} \times \frac{3}{7}$

2. Copy and complete these multiplications

(a) $\dfrac{4}{{}_3\cancel{15}} \times \dfrac{\cancel{5}^1}{7} = \dfrac{\square}{\square}$ (b) $\dfrac{\cancel{4}^1}{5} \times \dfrac{7}{\cancel{8}_2} = \dfrac{\square}{\square}$

3. Work out

(a) $\frac{3}{8} \times \frac{4}{5}$ (b) $\frac{2}{9} \times \frac{6}{7}$ (c) $\frac{5}{12} \times \frac{3}{10}$ (d) $\frac{5}{8} \times \frac{6}{15}$

(e) $\frac{5}{9} \times \frac{3}{4}$ (f) $\frac{4}{10} \times \frac{5}{12}$ (g) $\frac{3}{14} \times \frac{7}{10}$ (h) $\frac{7}{18} \times \frac{6}{35}$

4. Work out

(a) $\frac{2}{3}$ of 12   (b) $\frac{3}{4}$ of 20   (c) $\frac{1}{5}$ of $\frac{2}{3}$ (d) $\frac{2}{7}$ of $\frac{1}{2}$

5. The petrol tank of a mower holds $\frac{1}{2}$ litre. How much petrol is in the tank when it is $\frac{3}{5}$ full?

6. Copy and complete

(a) $8 = \square \times \frac{1}{2}$ (b) $\square \times \frac{1}{3} = 6$ (c) $\square \times \frac{1}{4} = 10$

(d) $\square \times \frac{1}{2} = \frac{1}{10}$ (e) $\frac{1}{9} = \square \times \frac{1}{3}$ (f) $\square \times \frac{2}{3} = 4$

7. Answer true or false:

(a) $\frac{1}{2}$ of $7 = \frac{7}{2}$ (b) $\frac{1}{5}$ of $20 = 20 \div \frac{1}{5}$

(c) $\frac{2}{3}$ of $\frac{1}{3} = \frac{2}{9}$

8. Of the 495 pupils at Cantonna College, $\frac{1}{3}$ travel by bus, $\frac{1}{5}$ travel by car and the rest cycle.
How many pupils cycle to the college?

9. Work out these divisions.

(a) $\frac{1}{2} \div \frac{5}{6}$ (b) $\frac{2}{3} \div \frac{7}{8}$ (c) $\frac{5}{9} \div \frac{3}{4}$ (d) $\frac{5}{7} \div \frac{1}{2}$

(e) $\frac{5}{9} \div \frac{1}{3}$ (f) $\frac{3}{5} \div \frac{9}{100}$ (g) $\frac{1}{4} \div \frac{1}{8}$ (h) $\frac{5}{12} \div \frac{5}{6}$

10. (a) Write the mixed number $2\frac{1}{2}$ as an improper fraction.
(b) Work out $2\frac{1}{2} \div \frac{1}{5}$.

11. Work out

(a) $1\frac{1}{2} \div \frac{1}{4}$ (b) $1\frac{1}{3} \div \frac{1}{6}$ (c) $\frac{5}{8} \div 1\frac{1}{2}$ (d) $1\frac{1}{4} \div 4$

(e) $5\frac{1}{2} \div 3$ (f) $\frac{3}{5} \div 2$ (g) $\frac{4}{7} \div 3$ (h) $\frac{5}{12} \div 3\frac{1}{3}$

Addition and subtraction

We know that $\frac{1}{3} + \frac{1}{3} = \frac{2}{3}$ and $\frac{2}{7} + \frac{3}{7} = \frac{5}{7}$

but $\frac{1}{5} + \frac{1}{3}$ is not so easy.

Method: (i) The fractions to be added must be written as fractions with the same denominator.
(ii) Mixed fractions should be written as top heavy fractions.

Examples: (a) $\frac{1}{5} + \frac{1}{3}$ (b) $\frac{3}{4} + \frac{1}{5}$ (c) $\frac{5}{6} - \frac{2}{9}$

$= \frac{3}{15} + \frac{5}{15}$ $= \frac{15}{20} + \frac{4}{20}$ $= \frac{15}{18} - \frac{4}{18}$

$= \frac{8}{15}$ $= \frac{19}{20}$ $= \frac{11}{18}$

Exercise 2

Work out and give the answer in its simplest form.

1. $\frac{1}{4} + \frac{3}{8}$ **2.** $\frac{3}{5} + \frac{1}{10}$ **3.** $\frac{2}{3} + \frac{1}{6}$ **4.** $\frac{5}{12} + \frac{1}{4}$

5. $\frac{7}{8} - \frac{1}{2}$ **6.** $\frac{1}{3} + \frac{1}{2}$ **7.** $\frac{3}{5} - \frac{1}{4}$ **8.** $\frac{4}{7} - \frac{1}{2}$

9. $\frac{2}{3} + \frac{1}{4}$ **10.** $\frac{2}{5} + \frac{1}{3}$ **11.** $\frac{1}{7} + \frac{1}{2}$ **12.** $\frac{1}{5} - \frac{1}{6}$

13. $\frac{2}{3} - \frac{5}{12}$ **14.** $\frac{7}{9} - \frac{1}{6}$ **15.** $\frac{4}{5} - \frac{2}{7}$ **16.** $\frac{7}{10} - \frac{1}{3}$

17. Write $1\frac{1}{2}$ as an improper fraction and work out $1\frac{1}{2} - \frac{5}{8}$.

18. Work out

(a) $1\frac{1}{4} - \frac{2}{5}$ (b) $1\frac{3}{4} - \frac{2}{3}$ (c) $3\frac{1}{4} + 1\frac{3}{5}$ (d) $2\frac{5}{6} + 1\frac{1}{4}$

19. Of his weekly income, Gary spends $\frac{1}{4}$ on food and $\frac{1}{3}$ on rent.
What fraction of his income is left for other things?

20. The algebraic fractions $\frac{3}{x} + \frac{2}{x}$ can be added to give $\frac{5}{x}$.
Simplify the following:

(a) $\frac{4}{n} + \frac{7}{n}$ (b) $\frac{10}{m} - \frac{7}{m}$ (c) $\frac{x}{n} + \frac{3x}{n}$

1.6 Geometrical reasoning

Properties of quadrilaterals

Square   Four equal sides;
All angles 90°;
Four lines of symmetry.

Rectangle (not square):   Two pairs of equal
and parallel sides;
All angles 90°;
Two lines of symmetry.

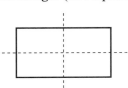

Rhombus: Four equal sides;
Opposite sides parallel;
Diagonals bisect at right angles;
Diagonals bisect angles of rhombus;
Two lines of symmetry.

Parallelogram: Two pairs of equal and parallel
sides;
Opposite angles equal;
No lines of symmetry (in general).

Trapezium: One pair of parallel sides.

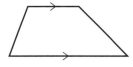

Kite: AB = AD, CB = CD;
Diagonals meet at 90°;
One line of symmetry.

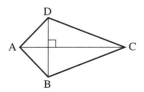

Arrowhead or **Delta**
Two pairs of adjacent edges of equal length.
One interior angle larger than 180°.
One line of symmetry.
Diagonals cross at right angles outside the shape.

For all quadrilaterals the sum of the interior angles is 360°.

Exercise 1

1. Name each of the following shapes:
   (a) ABEH
   (b) EFGH
   (c) CDFE

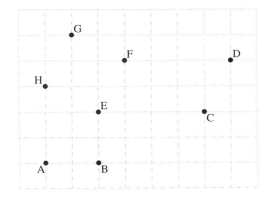

2. (a) Write down the coordinates of point D
     if ABCD is a kite
   (b) Write down the coordinates of point
     E if ABCE is a parallelogram
   (c) Write down the coordinates of point G
     if BCGF is an arrowhead.
     [There is more than one
     possible answer to part (c).]

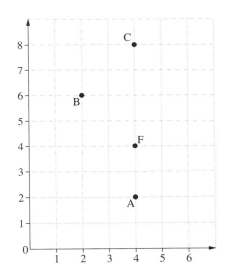

3. Copy the table and fill all the boxes with either 'Yes', 'No' or a number.

	How many lines of symmetry	How many pairs of opposite sides are parallel	Diagonals always equal?	Diagonals are perpendicular?
Square				
Rectangle				
Kite				
Rhombus				
Parallelogram				
Arrowhead				

4. Find the angle x.

(a)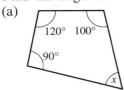

(b)

(c)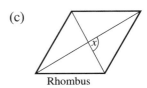

(d)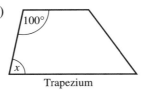

(e)

(f)

5. The diagram shows three vertices (corners) of a parallelogram. Copy the diagram and mark with crosses the *three* possible positions of the fourth vertex.

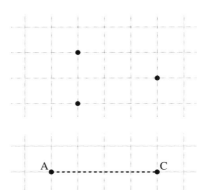

6. Line AC is one *diagonal* of a rhombus ABCD. Draw *two* possible rhombuses ABCD.

7. Suppose you cut along the diagonal of a rectangle to make two congruent triangles. Join the diagonals together in a different way. What shape is formed?

8. Suppose you had two identical isosceles triangles. Put the equal sides together to make as many different shapes as possible. Name the shapes formed.

9. An equilateral triangle has vertices P, Q, R.
   (a) Suppose the vertex P moves perpendicular to QR.

   What different types of triangle can be made?
   Can you make: a right-angled triangle;
   an obtuse-angled triangle;
   a scalene triangle?
   (b) If the vertex P moves *parallel* to QR, what different types of triangle can be made?

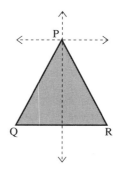

Polygons

The word 'polygon' is normally used for flat shapes with 5 or more edges.
A quadrilateral is, in fact, a polygon with 4 edges.

The table shows the names of the more common polygons.

A *regular* polygon has edges of equal length and all its angles are equal.

Name	Number of edges
Pentagon	5
Hexagon	6
Heptagon	7
Octagon	8
Nonagon	9
Decagon	10

Exercise 2

1. The diagram shows a pentagon in which we have started to draw in the diagonals. Draw your own diagram of a pentagon and find how many diagonals there are altogether.

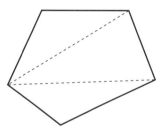

2. Draw a hexagon and show that it has nine diagonals.

3. How many lines of symmetry has a regular pentagon?

4. How many lines of symmetry has a regular hexagon?

5. What is the name for a regular polygon with
   (a) four sides,
   (b) three sides?

6. A trapezium has one pair of parallel sides.
   Draw three *pentagons* with:
   (a) one pair of parallel sides,
   (b) two pairs of parallel sides,
   (c) three right angles.

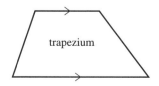
trapezium

7. Sketch a diagram of a regular hexagon.
   Are all the diagonals the same length?

Angles in polygons

- We already know that angles in a triangle add up to 180° and angles in a quadrilateral add up to 360°.

  What happens in polygons with a greater number of sides?

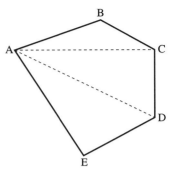

- First draw any pentagon (5 sided shape). Choose one of the corners, A say, and join this to all the other corners. (B and E will already be joined by the sides of the pentagon).

  This divides the pentagon into 3 triangles. As we already know that the angles in each of these triangles adds up to 180° the angles in our pentagon must add up to:

  $$3 \times 180° = 540°$$

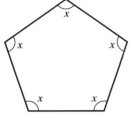

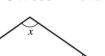
The angles in a pentagon add up to 540°

If we had started with a *regular* pentagon all the sides would have been the same length and all the angles would be the same. As there are 5 equal angles, each angle $= 540 \div 5$
$= 108°$

Exercise 3

1. Copy and complete the following table. Split up polygons with 6, 8 and 10 sides into triangles as in the example above.

   Look for a pattern in the numbers and try to complete the rest of the table without drawing the polygon first.

Number of sides	Number of triangles	Total of interior angles	Interior angle of regular polygon
3	1	$1 \times 180° = 180°$	$180° \div 3 = 60°$
4	2	$2 \times 180° = 360°$	$360° \div 4 = 90°$
5	3	$3 \times 180° = 540°$	$540° \div 5 = 108°$
6			
8			
10			
20			
n			

Teachers note:

The result for the sum of the angles in a polygon with n sides obtained from the bottom row is needed in subsequent questions

Exercise 4

Use the formula below for a polygon with *n* sides.

sum of interior angles $= (n - 2) \times 180°$

1. Find the sum of the angles in a polygon with 7 sides.

2. Find the sum of the angles in a polygon with
   (a) 9 sides
   (b) 12 sides
   (c) 102 sides.

3. Find the angles marked with letters.

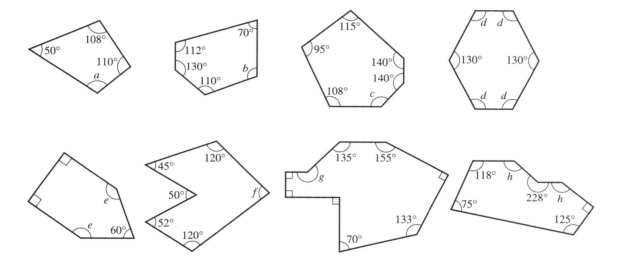

Exterior angles of a polygon

The exterior angle of a polygon is the angle between a produced side and the adjacent side of the polygon. The word 'produced' in this context means 'extended'.

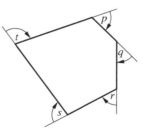

If we put all the exterior angles together we can see that the sum of the angles is 360°. This is true for any polygon.

The sum of the exterior angles of a polygon $= 360°$

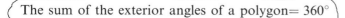

Note:
(a) In a regular polygon all exterior angles are equal.
(b) For a regular polygon with n sides, each exterior angle $= \dfrac{360°}{n}$.

The exterior angle is made by extending a side of the polygon.
We can see that at any vertex the sum of the interior and exterior angles is $180°$

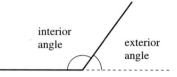

Exercise 5

1. Find the angles marked with letters.

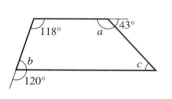
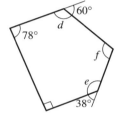
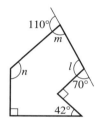
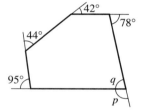

2. (a) Calculate the size of each exterior angle for a regular hexagon.
   (b) Write down the size of the interior angle for the same shape.

3. A decagon has 10 sides. Find the size of each exterior angle of a regular decagon.

4. (a) Find the exterior angles of regular polygons with
      (i) 9 sides   (ii) 18 sides   (iii) 45 sides   (iv) 60 sides
   (b) Find the interior angle of the above polygons.

5. Each exterior angle of a regular polygon is $18°$. How many sides has the polygon?

6. The sides of a regular polygon subtend angles of $18°$ at the centre of the polygon. How many sides has the polygon?

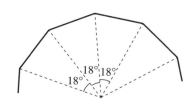

Part 2

2.1 Using a calculator

Order of operations

Here is an apparently simple calculation

$$4 \cdot 52 + 3 \cdot 5 \times 6 \cdot 3$$

Working left to right on a calculator, press

$$\boxed{4 \cdot 52} \;\; \boxed{+} \;\; \boxed{3 \cdot 5} \;\; \boxed{\times} \;\; \boxed{6 \cdot 3} \;\; \boxed{=}$$

Depending on what make of calculator you use, you may get 50·526 or you may get 26·57. Which is correct?

Where there is a mixture of operations to be performed to avoid uncertainty you must follow these rules: (a) work out brackets first
(b) work out ÷, × before +, −.

Some people use the word 'BIDMAS' to help them remember the correct order of operations.

Brackets
Indices
Divide
Multiply
Add
Subtract

Here are four examples

- $8 + 6 \div 6 = 8 + 1 = 9$
- $20 - 8 \times 2 = 20 - 16 = 4$
- $(13 - 7) \div (6 - 4) = 6 \div 2 = 3$
- $20 - 8 \div (5 + 3) = 20 - 8 \div 8 = 19$

Exercise 1

In Questions **1** to **20** do not use a calculator to work out the answer.

1. $13 + 9 \div 3$
2. $40 - 5 \times 7$
3. $8 \times 3 - 14$
4. $(8 + 3) \times 6$
5. $15 - (7 + 5)$
6. $8 + 3 \times 2$
7. $17 - 12 \div 4$
8. $24 \div (1 + 7)$
9. $3 \times 4 + 5 \times 2$
10. $30 \div 3 + 5 \times 4$
11. $3 + 20 \div 2$
12. $(10 \div 2) \div 4$
13. $16 - (8 + 3 \times 2)$
14. $(9 \div 1 - 2) \times 4$
15. $3 \times 5 - 12 \div 2$
16. $8 \times 2 - 4 \div 2$
17. $\dfrac{9 - 5}{10 - 8}$
18. $\dfrac{10 + 3 \times 2}{8 \div 2}$
19. $\dfrac{36 - 12 \div 2}{5 + 1}$
20. $\dfrac{(6 + 5) \times 2}{12 - 5 \div 5}$

KALK#1 ALLMONOV + CAMPBELLSKI®

MODE ▶	① DEGREES	④ NORMAL	⑦ OOH, ER!
	② GET ON!	⑤ BARMY	⑧ GAMES...
⓪ COMPUTE	③ WEAK MIND	⑥ OUI OU NON!	⑨ *!?*!??HELP

SHIFT

	MODE	M IN	MR	OFF
$x!$ 1/x	$^{\wedge}Pr$ √	$^{\wedge}Cr$ x^2	$x^{1/y}$ x^y	10^x LOG
d/c a b/c	E^x In	SIN^{-1} SIN	COS^{-1} COS	TAN^{-1} TAN
$\sqrt[3]{}$ +/−	▶	[(---	---)]	← ° ' "
7	8	9	C	AC ON
4	5	6	×	÷
1	2	3	+	−
0	.	π EXP	% =	M− M+

In Questions **21** to **35** use a calculator and give the answer correct to two decimal places.

21. $8{\cdot}51 + 8{\cdot}7 \div 3{\cdot}2$ **22.** $14{\cdot}82 + 1{\cdot}24 \times 1{\cdot}1$ **23.** $7{\cdot}3 \times 1{\cdot}9 - 5{\cdot}04$

24. $9{\cdot}764 + (8{\cdot}2 \div 2{\cdot}93)$ **25.** $11{\cdot}73 \div 9{\cdot}2 - 0{\cdot}971$ **26.** $(8{\cdot}7 \div 9) + 1{\cdot}9$

27. $(111{\cdot}7 \div 4{\cdot}5 - 6) \times 1{\cdot}9$ **28.** $12{\cdot}2 + 3{\cdot}7 \times 3{\cdot}7$ **29.** $9{\cdot}25 \div (1{\cdot}4 - 0{\cdot}07)$

30. $1{\cdot}234 + \dfrac{8{\cdot}5}{9{\cdot}2}$ **31.** $\dfrac{8{\cdot}96 + 2{\cdot}761}{4{\cdot}02}$ **32.** $\dfrac{8{\cdot}43}{3{\cdot}3} - 2{\cdot}04$

33. $8{\cdot}61 + 1{\cdot}9 \times 0{\cdot}6$ **34.** $0{\cdot}31 + (12{\cdot}2 \div 7)$ **35.** $62{\cdot}4 \times 0{\cdot}13 - 4{\cdot}11$

Using the memory

In complicated calculations you have to think ahead to decide in which order to perform the operations. In Book 8i we used the brackets buttons. Here we look at the memory buttons.

$\boxed{\text{Min}}$ Puts the number displayed into the memory. It automatically clears any number already in the memory when it puts in the new number.

$\boxed{\text{MR}}$ Recalls the number in the memory.

To *clear* the memory we will press $\boxed{0}\ \boxed{\text{Min}}$.

Many calculators will keep a number stored in the memory even when they are switched off. A letter 'M' on the display shows that the memory does contain a number.

The $\boxed{\text{Min}}$ key is very useful because it *automatically* clears any number already in the memory when it puts in the new number.

So if you pressed $\boxed{13{\cdot}2}\ \boxed{\text{Min}}\ \boxed{6{\cdot}5}\ \boxed{\text{Min}}$, the number in the memory would be 6·5. The 13·2 is effectively 'lost'.

Work out, correct to 2 decimal places.

(a) $\dfrac{8{\cdot}97}{1{\cdot}6 - 0{\cdot}973}$ (b) $8{\cdot}51 - \left(\dfrac{3{\cdot}24}{1{\cdot}73}\right)$

Work out the bottom line first.   Work out the brackets first.

$\boxed{1{\cdot}6}\ \boxed{-}\ \boxed{0{\cdot}973}\ \boxed{=}\ \boxed{\text{Min}}$ $\boxed{3{\cdot}24}\ \boxed{\div}\ \boxed{1{\cdot}73}\ \boxed{=}\ \boxed{\text{Min}}$

$\boxed{8{\cdot}97}\ \boxed{\div}\ \boxed{\text{MR}}\ \boxed{=}$ $\boxed{8{\cdot}51}\ \boxed{-}\ \boxed{\text{MR}}\ \boxed{=}$

Answer = 14·31 to 2 d.p.   Answer = 6·64 to 2 d.p.

A very common error occurs when people forget to press the $\boxed{=}$ button at the end of the calculaton.

Exercise 2

Work out and give the answer correct to 2 decimal places.

1. $\dfrac{5\cdot63}{2\cdot8-1\cdot71}$ **2.** $\dfrac{11\cdot5}{5\cdot24+1\cdot57}$ **3.** $\dfrac{8\cdot27}{2\cdot9\times1\cdot35}$

4. $\dfrac{3\cdot7-2\cdot41}{1\cdot9+0\cdot72}$ **5.** $\dfrac{8\cdot5+9\cdot3}{12\cdot9-8\cdot72}$ **6.** $\dfrac{0\cdot97\times3\cdot85}{1\cdot24+4\cdot63}$

7. $14\cdot5-\left(\dfrac{1\cdot9}{0\cdot7}\right)$ **8.** $8\cdot41-3\cdot2\times1\cdot76$ **9.** $11\cdot62-\dfrac{6\cdot3}{9\cdot8}$

10. $\dfrac{9\cdot84\times0\cdot751}{6\cdot3\times0\cdot95}$ **11.** $5\cdot62+1\cdot98+\dfrac{1\cdot2}{4\cdot5}$ **12.** $8\cdot5-\dfrac{8\cdot9}{11\cdot6}$

13. $\dfrac{6\cdot3}{4\cdot2}+\dfrac{8\cdot2}{11\cdot9}$ **14.** $\dfrac{8\cdot43+1\cdot99}{9\cdot6-1\cdot73}$ **15.** $\dfrac{17\cdot6}{8\cdot4}-\dfrac{1\cdot92}{8\cdot41}$

16. $25\cdot1-4\cdot2^2$ **17.** $(9\cdot8-4\cdot43)^2$ **18.** $18\cdot7-2\cdot33^2$

19. $8\cdot21^2+1\cdot67^2$ **20.** $9\cdot23^2-7\cdot42^2$ **21.** $16\cdot1-1\cdot1^2$

22. $\dfrac{16\cdot1}{4\cdot7}-1\cdot8^2$ **23.** $\left(\dfrac{17\cdot2}{9\cdot8}-1\cdot2\right)^2$ **24.** $9\cdot9-8\cdot3\times0\cdot075$

25. $1\cdot21-\dfrac{9}{14^2}$ **26.** $3\cdot7^2+\dfrac{11\cdot4}{1\cdot7}$ **27.** $\dfrac{11\cdot7-3\cdot73}{2\cdot45^2}$

28. $\dfrac{8\cdot94}{4\cdot8+1\cdot7^2}$ **29.** $\dfrac{3\cdot21}{8\cdot2-4\cdot11}$ **30.** $\dfrac{116\cdot7}{8\cdot1^2+32}$

31. $8\cdot7+\dfrac{8\cdot2}{9\cdot7}+\dfrac{4\cdot1}{5\cdot6}$ **32.** $8\cdot5-(1\cdot6^2+1\cdot9^2)$ **33.** $8\cdot3+\dfrac{1\cdot9}{8\cdot4}-\dfrac{1\cdot7}{6\cdot5}$

34. $3\cdot2+\left(3\cdot2+\dfrac{1\cdot4}{5}\right)^2$ **35.** $\dfrac{3\cdot4}{1\cdot6}+\left(\dfrac{2\cdot1}{1\cdot3}\right)^2$ **36.** $\left(8\cdot2-\dfrac{1}{8\cdot2}\right)\times8\cdot2$

Other useful buttons

$\boxed{M+}$ Adds the number to the current memory. This key is useful when several numbers are to be added together.

$\boxed{x^y}$ Raises the number to a power. For 5^3 press $\boxed{5}\,\boxed{x^y}\,\boxed{3}\,\boxed{=}$.

(a) $5 \cdot 2 + (7 \cdot 2 \times 1 \cdot 4) + (8 \cdot 63 \times 1 \cdot 9)$

| 0 | Min | 5·2 | M+ | 7·2 | × | 1·4 | = | M+ | 8·63 | × | 1·9 | = | M+ | MR |

Answer = 31·7 (to 1 d.p.)

(b) $15 \cdot 2 \times 6 \cdot 3 - 4 \cdot 2^3$

| 4·2 | x^y | 3 | = | Min | 15·2 | × | 6·3 | = | − | MR | = |

Answer = 21·7 (to 1 d.p.)

(c) $\left(\dfrac{1 \cdot 71}{8 \cdot 72 - 5 \cdot 63} \right)^3$

| 8·72 | − | 5·63 | = | Min | 1·71 | ÷ | MR | = | x^y | 3 | = |

Answer = 0·17 (to 2 d.p.)

Exercise 3

Work out, correct to 2 decimal places, unless told otherwise.

Use the | M+ | button in Questions **1** to **10**. Don't forget to clear the memory each time!

1. $(1 \cdot 3 \times 2 \cdot 4) + (5 \cdot 3 \times 0 \cdot 7) + (8 \cdot 6 \times 0 \cdot 61) + 11 \cdot 7$

2. $(0 \cdot 8 \times 0 \cdot 7) + (1 \cdot 1 \times 3 \cdot 5) + 6 \cdot 23 + (1 \cdot 9 \times 0 \cdot 8)$

3. $(1 \cdot 8 \times 1 \cdot 9 \times 3 \cdot 1) + (0 \cdot 91 \times 5 \cdot 6) + (4 \cdot 71 \times 1 \cdot 9)$

4. $(8 \cdot 9 \times 1 \cdot 5) + 7 \cdot 1^2 + 5 \cdot 3^2 + 31 \cdot 4$

5. $8 \cdot 21 + (9 \cdot 71 \times 2 \cdot 3) + (8 \cdot 2 \times 1 \cdot 4) + 2 \cdot 67$

6. $(8 \cdot 9 \times 1 \cdot 1) + (1 \cdot 2 \times 1 \cdot 3 \times 1 \cdot 4) + (0 \cdot 76 \times 3 \cdot 68)$

In Questions **7** to **10** find the total bill, correct to the nearest penny.

7. 5 tins at 42p each
4 jars of jam at 69p each
48 eggs at £1·55/dozen
3 packets of tea at £1·19 each
4 grapefruit at 33p each

8. 200 g of cheese at £5·20/kg
1 bottle of ketchup at £1·19
3 jars of coffee at £2·45 each
4 lemons at 29p each
8lb potatoes at 32p/lb

9. 14 bolts at 22p each
30 m of cable at 15p/metre
3 sacks of fertilizer at £5·35 each
200 tiles at £2·30 for 10
5 plugs at 48p each

10. 1 tube of glue at £1·35
3 tins of paint at £4·20 each
100 m of wire at 11p/metre
100 g of nails at £8/kg
3 boxes of seed at £3·35 each

In Questions **11** to **19** use the x^y button, where needed.

11. $3 \cdot 7^3$ **12.** $2 \cdot 1^4$ **13.** $3 \cdot 1^5 + 112$

14. $1 \cdot 64^5$ **15.** $(1 \cdot 81 + 2 \cdot 43)^4$ **16.** $19 \cdot 8 + 1 \cdot 96^3$

17. $1 \cdot 7^3 + 2 \cdot 4^3$ **18.** $200 - 3 \cdot 7^4$ **19.** $3 \cdot 2 + 3 \cdot 2^2 + 3 \cdot 2^3$

In Questions **20** to **34** think ahead and use your calculator as efficiently as possible.

20. $\dfrac{5 \cdot 65}{1 \cdot 21 + 3 \cdot 7}$ **21.** $\dfrac{8 \cdot 7}{13} + \dfrac{4 \cdot 9}{15}$ **22.** $14 \cdot 6 - (3 \cdot 9 \times 2 \cdot 62)$

23. $12 \cdot 94 - \sqrt{8 \cdot 97}$ **24.** $\dfrac{5 \cdot 41 + 7 \cdot 82}{9 \cdot 82 - 3 \cdot 99}$ **25.** $\sqrt{\dfrac{100 \cdot 9}{9 \cdot 81 + 56}}$

26. $11 \cdot 2\%$ of $9 \cdot 6^3$ **27.** $\frac{2}{7}$ of $\left(\dfrac{4 \cdot 2}{1 \cdot 95 - 0 \cdot 713}\right)$ **28.** $\frac{1}{6} + \frac{1}{7} + \frac{1}{8} + \frac{1}{9}$

29. $\dfrac{\sqrt{8 \cdot 74} + \sqrt{7 \cdot 05}}{\sqrt{3 \cdot 14} + \sqrt{2 \cdot 76}}$ **30.** $\dfrac{900}{101 - 2 \cdot 9^4}$ **31.** $(15\%$ of $22 \cdot 36)^3$

32. 18% of $9 \cdot 1\%$ of 1150 **33.** $2 \cdot 8^5 - \sqrt{\dfrac{9 \cdot 7}{11 \cdot 4}}$ **34.** $\frac{2}{3}$ of $\left(\dfrac{9 \cdot 81}{1 \cdot 25^2}\right)^3$

Calculator words

- When you hold a calculator display upside down some numbers appear to form words: | 4506 | spells "Gosh"

  | 0.70 | spells "Old"

  (ignoring the decimal point)

Exercise 4

Translate this passage using a calculator and the clues below:

'$\underline{①}$!', $\underline{②}$, $\underline{③}$, climbing out of $\underline{④}$. 'It's raining. I can't take $\underline{⑤}$ and $\underline{⑥}$ for a walk now.' $\underline{⑦}$ and $\underline{⑧}$ were her $\underline{⑨}$ and they loved to $\underline{⑩}$ up the $\underline{⑪}$ and roll about, covering their $\underline{⑫}$ $\underline{⑬}$ in mud.

From the window of her small $\underline{⑭}$, she saw a lady coming down the $\underline{⑮}$. '$\underline{⑯}$ $\underline{⑰}$!' said $\underline{⑱}$. 'It's $\underline{⑲}$, come to $\underline{⑳}$ her $\underline{㉑}$ $\underline{㉒}$. I'll ask her in for a chat.' ' $\underline{㉓}$, $\underline{㉔}$. $\underline{㉕}$! I'm wetting your floor,' $\underline{㉖}$ $\underline{㉗}$, taking off her coat and $\underline{㉘}$ and giving $\underline{㉙}$ the basket of $\underline{㉚}$ $\underline{㉛}$ $\underline{㉜}$. 'I'll $\underline{㉝}$ the eggs now', said $\underline{㉞}$. 'Do you want some?'

'Yes please' smiled $\underline{㉟}$. 'I'll eat anything that is $\underline{㊱}$.' 'Did you know that the $\underline{㊲}$ of the $\underline{㊳}$

garage was ill and $\underset{\text{(39)}}{}$ so the garage is closed until it is $\underset{\text{(40)}}{}$ to someone $\underset{\text{(41)}}{}$, ' $\underset{\text{(42)}}{}$. The $\underset{\text{(43)}}{}$ $\underset{\text{(44)}}{}$ are ready.' 'Is that a new $\underset{\text{(45)}}{}$ in your garden?' asked $\underset{\text{(46)}}{}$. Gardening was one of $\underset{\text{(47)}}{}$ $\underset{\text{(48)}}{}$ and she could $\underset{\text{(49)}}{}$ away hours with her plants and her pet $\underset{\text{(50)}}{}$. As it wasn't raining anymore she decided to let the $\underset{\text{(51)}}{}$ $\underset{\text{(52)}}{}$ in the garden. $\underset{\text{(53)}}{}$ had to go, so she put on her $\underset{\text{(54)}}{}$ $\underset{\text{(55)}}{}$ and coat. Picking up her basket, $\underset{\text{(56)}}{}$ $\underset{\text{(57)}}{}$, 'My basket has so many $\underset{\text{(58)}}{}$. It doesn't $\underset{\text{(59)}}{}$ $\underset{\text{(60)}}{}$ properly anymore. It $\underset{\text{(61)}}{}$.' With that $\underset{\text{(62)}}{}$ left, saying $\underset{\text{(63)}}{}$, just in time to $\underset{\text{(64)}}{}$ another downpour.

Clues to passage

1: $2 \times 2 \times 2 \times 5$

2: $0.4 - 0.05085$

3: $22 \times 23 \times 24 \times 25 + 15\,230$

4: $0.6^2 + (2 \times 0.1 \times 0.1)$

5: 0.3×0.5

6: $(9 \times 10 \times 11) - (2 \times 7 \times 13)$

7: $0.4^2 - 0.1^2$

8: $(10^2 + 1) \times 2^3$

9: $1234 + 5678 - 1012$

10: $(5 \times 6 \times 5 \times 6) + (1 + 2 + 3 + 4)$

11: $203 \times 7 \times 5$

12: $1000 - (3^4 + 1)$

13: $728 \times 729 + 8 \times 37$

14: $3 \times 13 \times 10^3 + (3.5 \div 0.5)$

15: $2570 + 2571 + 2572 + 1^{74}$

16: $10^3 \div 5^2$

17: $9 \div 1000$

18: $333\,333 - 12345 - 2158$

19: $(67 \times 68 \times 69) + (34 \times 35) - (2^4)$

20: $5 \times 7 \times (11 \times 20 + 1)$

21: $5 \times 5 \times 5 \times 5 \times 2 \times 2 \times 2 \times 7 + 9$

22: $6000 - 7$

23: $0.1234 + 0.65$

24: $11 \times 2 \times 8 \times 3 \times 23 \times 5^2 + (2 \times 7615)$

25: $(3^2 - 1^2) \times 5$

26: $5 \times 3 \times 23$

27: $0.38 - 0.000081$

28: $123 \times 432 - 91$

29: $320\,000 - 1170$

30: $30 \times 200 - 8 + 1$

31: $567 + 345 - 567$

32: $0.7 + 0.004 + 0.03$

33: 1777×2^2

34: $321\,123 - 2293$

35: $561 \times 562 + 2^8$

36: $377\,777 + 321 + 5$

37: $33\,048 \div (4.7 + 1.3)$

38: $12345 + (5 \times 13 \times 10^3)$

39: $0.31 + 0.00034$

40: $0.047 \times 5 \times 3$

41: $60^2 - 3^3$

42: $68 \times 69 \times 70 + (22 + 45) \times 100$

43: $0.61^2 - 0.00102$

44: $10^4 - 4007$

45: $(23 \times 5 \times 3) \div 1000$

46: $105\,180 + 105\,181 + 105\,177$

47: $47 \times 48 \times 49 \times 50 - 208\,370$

48: $(23 \times 10^2 \times 209 \times 11) + 31\,104$

49: $503 \times \sqrt{(108 \div 3)}$

50: $448 \times 449 \times 450 - 79\,366$

51: $41\,300 \div (0.32 + 0.61 + 6.07)$

52: $(0.7 \div 0.1) + (5 \times 7 \times 10^3)$

53: $16^2 + 562 \times 561$

54: $0.33333 + 0.04001$

55: $(10^4 + 609) \times 5$

56: $(4^2 - 1^2) \times (30 - 11)$

57: $0.6^2 - 0.1^2 - 0.00085$

58: $(999 - 40) \times 2^3 \times 7$

59: $0.011 \times \sqrt{4096}$

60: $5678 + 630 \div 2$

61: $1 - 0.3 + 0.000551$

62: $315\,513 + (10^3 \div 40)$

63: $146 \times 147 \times 148 + (3 \times 1211)$

64: $[1001 \div (7 \times 11)] \times 10^3 \times 3$

Crossword 1

Copy the crossword pattern and complete the puzzle using the clues
below. Remember to turn your calculator upside down to read the
'words'. You write *words* in the puzzle not numbers.

Across
1. $(3 \times 13 \times 10^4) - 10^4 - 9^2$ funny laugh
4. $\sqrt{0.25}$ and because of that ...
5. $\frac{3}{8} - \frac{9}{200}$ needs another letter.
6. 2nd prime $\times$ 7th prime   currently being
8. $\frac{1}{4} + \frac{9}{20} + \frac{1}{200}$ you're on your own
10. $5((50 \times 30) + 43)$ by the window ...
11. $5 \times 23 \times 7$ crying

Down
2. $60 \times 90 - 7 \times 13$ almost gone
3. $0.75 \times 10^6 - (5 \times 7259)$ pretty hot stuff
7. $5(10^4 + 5^4 - 4^2)$ they're made for walking
9. $(20 \times 35) + (5 \times 2)$ used for cooking.

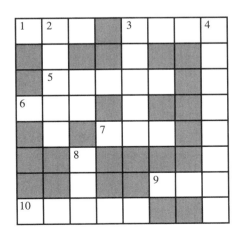

Crossword 2

Copy and complete this crossword.

Across
1. $(2 \times 3^2 \times 5^2) + 1$ sort of ...
3. $\frac{1}{2}$ of 9000 $+ \frac{1}{8}$ of 48   I am surprised
5. $41 \times 42 \times 43 - 229$ telling lies
6. $7 \div (100 \div 2)$ placed out of view
7. $5^4 + 12$ tables usually have four
9. $(11^2 - 20) \times 5$ help!
10. $\frac{15}{200} + (11 \div 10\,000)$ it's cold in here

Down
2. $\left(\frac{4}{10}\right)^2 + \frac{1}{100} + \frac{5}{10\,000}$ three dimensional object
3. $(600^2 - 6640) \div 10$ Better than guard dogs
4. $(5.5 \times 10^7) + 270^2 + 12\,234$ In charge
8. $9^3 + 6 \times 7$ unwell

2.2 Construction and scale drawing

A Perpendicular bisector of a line segment AB.

With centres A and B draw two arcs.
The perpendicular bisector is shown as a broken line.

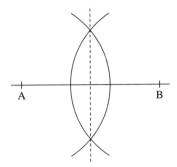

B Perpendicular from point P to a line

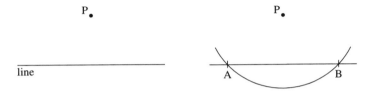

With centre P draw an arc
to cut the line at A and B.

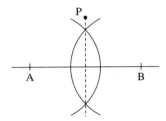

Construct the perpendicular
bisector of AB.

C Bisector of an angle

With centre A draw arc PQ.
With centres at P and Q draw two more arcs.
The angle bisector is then drawn.

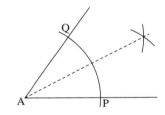

Exercise 1 [use plain unlined paper]

Use only a pencil, a straight edge and a pair of compasses.

1. Draw a horizontal line AB of the length 6 cm. Construct the perpendicular bisector of AB.

2. Draw a vertical line CD of length 8 cm. Construct the perpendicular bisector of CD.

3. Draw a line and a point P about 4 cm from the line. Construct the line which passes through P which is perpendicular to the line.

see construction **B** above

4. (a) Using a set square, draw a right-angled triangle ABC as shown. For greater accuracy draw lines slightly longer than 12 cm and 5 cm and *then* mark the points A, B and C.

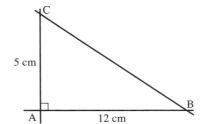

(b) *Construct* the perpendicular bisector of AB.

(c) Construct the perpendicular bisector of AC

(d) If done accurately, your two lines from (b) and (c) should cross exactly on the line BC.

5. This is the construction of a perpendicular from a point P on a line, using ruler and compasses.

(a) With centre P, draw arcs to cut the line at A and B.

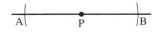

(b) Now construct the perpendicular bisector of AB.

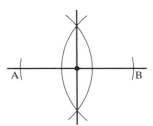

6. This is the construction of a triangle given 'RHS'. [Right angle, hypotenuse and side]

(a) Draw a line and construct a perpendicular at point P as in Question **5**.

(b) Complete the triangle, given PQ = 5 cm and RQ = 8 cm.

(c) Measure the side PR.

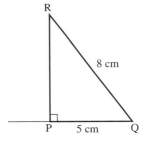

7. Construct the triangle shown, using ruler and compasses. BC = 7 cm and AC = 9 cm.

Measure the side AB

8. An 8 m ladder rests against a wall with its foot 3 m away from the wall. Construct a scale diagram and measure how far up the wall the ladder reaches.

52

9. Draw an angle of about 40°. Construct the bisector of the angle.

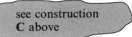

see construction
C above

10. Draw an angle of about 100°. Construct the bisector of the angle.

11. Draw any triangle ABC and then construct the bisectors of angles A, B and C. If done accurately the three bisectors should all pass through one point.

In Questions **12** to **14** a protractor may be used if necessary. Use a scale of 1 cm to represent 1 km.

12. A ship sails 6 km due north and then a further 7 km due west. Find the distance of the ship from its starting point.

13. A ship sails 8 km due east and then a further 5 km north-east. Find the distance of the ship from its starting point.

14. A ship sails 10 km due south and then a further 8 km on a bearing 070°. How far is the ship now from its starting point?

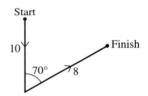

15. A grass playing field in the shape of the quadrilateral shown is to be sprayed with weedkiller at the rate of 3 grams of weedkiller per square metre of grass.

   (a) Draw an accurate scale drawing of the field using a scale of 1 cm to 10 cm.

   (b) Measure DE and BF to find the heights of the triangles.

   (c) Find the areas of the triangles ABC and ACD and hence find the total area of the playing field in square metres.

   (d) Find how much weedkiller is needed for this field. Give your answer to the nearest kg.

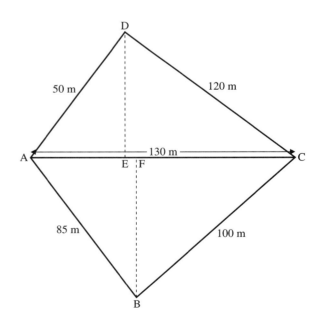

2.3 Scatter graphs

Sometimes it is important to discover if there is a connection or relationship between two sets of data.

Examples

- Are more ice creams sold when the weather is hot?

- Do tall people have higher pulse rates?

- Are people who are good at maths also good at science?

- Does watching TV improve examination results?

If there is a relationship, it will be easy to spot if your data is plotted on a scatter diagram – that is a graph in which one set of data is plotted on the horizontal axis and the other on the vertical axis.

- Here is a scatter graph showing the price of pears and the quantity sold.

- We can see a connection: when the price was high the sales were low and when the price went down the sales increased.

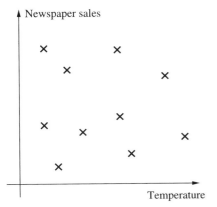

- This scatter graph shows the sales of a newspaper and the temperature. We can see there is *no connection* between the two variables.

Correlation

The word correlation describes how things *co-relate*. There is correlation between two sets of data if there is a connection or relationship.

The correlation between two sets of data can be positive or negative and it can be strong or weak as indicated by the scatter graphs below.

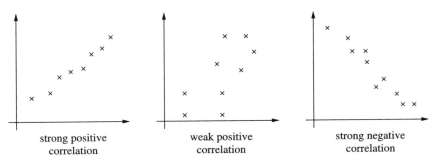

| strong positive correlation | weak positive correlation | strong negative correlation |

When the correlation is positive the points are around a line which slopes upwards to the right. When the correlation is negative the 'line' slopes downwards to the right.
When the correlation is strong the points are bunched close to a line through their midst. When the correlation is weak the points are more scattered.

It is important to realise that often there is *no* correlation between two sets of data.

If, for example, we take a group of students and plot their maths test results against their time to run 800 m, the graph might look like the one on the right. A common mistake in this topic is to 'see' a correlation on a scatter graph where none exists.

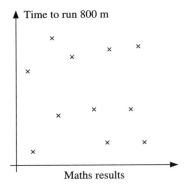

There is also *no* correlation in these two scatter graphs.

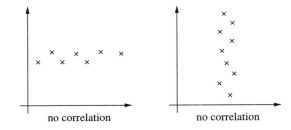

Exercise 1

1. Make the following measurements
   for everyone in your class:
   height   (nearest cm)
   armspan   (nearest cm)
   head circumference (nearest cm)
   hand span   (nearest cm)
   pulse rate   (beats/minute)

   For greater consistency of
   measuring, one person (or
   perhaps 2 people) should do all
   the measurements of one kind
   (except on themselves!)

   Enter all the measurements in a table,
   either on the board or on a sheet of paper.

Name	Height	Armspan	Head
Roger	161	165	56 cm
Liz	150	148	49 cm
Gill			

   (a) Draw the scatter graphs shown below

   (i) arm span / height

   (ii) hand span / pulse

   (b) Describe the correlation, if any, in the scatter graphs you
   drew in part (a).

   (c) (i)   Draw a scatter graph of two measurements where you
   think there might be positive correlation.
        (ii) Was there indeed a positive correlation?

2. Plot the points given on a scatter graph, with s across the page
   and p up the page. Draw axes with values from 0 to 20.
   Describe the correlation, if any, between the values of s and p.
   [i.e. 'strong negative', 'weak positive' etc.]

(a)

s	7	16	4	12	18	6	20	4	10	13
p	8	15	6	12	17	9	18	7	10	14

(b)

s	3	8	12	15	16	5	6	17	9
p	4	2	10	17	5	10	17	11	15

(c)

s	11	1	16	7	2	19	8	4	13	18
p	5	12	7	14	17	1	11	8	11	5

3. Describe the correlation; if any, in these scatter graphs.

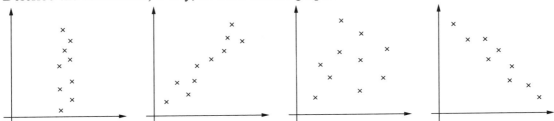

4. The table shows the marks of 7 students in the two papers of a science examination.

Paper 1	35	10	60	17	43	55	49
Paper 2	26	15	40	15	30	34	35

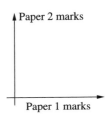

(a) Plot the marks on a scatter diagram, using a scale of 1 cm to 5 marks.

(b) A student got a mark of 25 on paper 1 but missed paper 2. What would you expect her to get on paper 2?

5. The table shows the mean weight of the apples from a certain apple tree together with the latitude of the farm where the tree was growing

Latitude (°N)	37	50	32	45	36	30	44
Mean weight of apples (g)	100	70	115	75	110	120	80

(a) Draw a scatter graph, using a scale of 1 cm to 5 g across the page and 2 cm to 5° up the page.

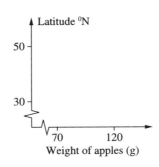

(b) What would you expect the mean weight of the apples to be on a farm at latitude 42°N?

6. Plot the points given on a scatter graph, with *m* across the page and *t* up the page. Draw axes with values from 0 to 20.

m	5	16	20	2	18	16	4	7
t	12	6	3	14	4	4	12	10

What value would you expect for *t* when *m* is 12?

7. The following data gives the marks of 11 students in a French test and in a German test.

French	15	36	36	22	23	27	43	22	43	40	26
German	6	28	35	18	28	28	37	9	41	45	17

(a) Plot this data on a scatter graph, with the French marks on the horizontal axis.

(b) Estimate the German mark of a student who got 30 in French.

8. A professional golfer was thinking about the factors which might affect his golf scores. He drew the three graphs below.

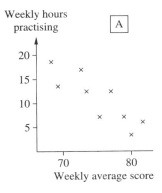

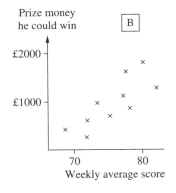

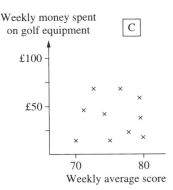

[N.B. In golf a score of 70 is *better* than a score of 80!]

(a) What does graph A show about the relationship between the weekly hours practising and his weekly average score?

(b) What does graph B show about the relationship between the amount of prize money he could win and his weekly average score?

(c) One week he spent 15 hours practising and he spent £50 on golf equipment. Explain whether or not you could estimate the average score for that week.

2.4 Solving equations

The main rule when solving equations is

'Do the same thing to both sides'.

You can *add* the same thing to both sides.
You can *subtract* the same thing from both sides.
You can *multiply* both sides by the same number.
You can *divide* both sides by the same number.

Solve the equations. The operations circled are performed on both sides.

(a) $3x - 1 = 5$
$(+1) \ (+1)$
$3x = 6$
$(\div 3) \ (\div 3)$
$x = 2$

(b) $2x + 3 = 4$
$(-3) \ (-3)$
$2x = 1$
$(\div 2) \ (\div 2)$
$x = \frac{1}{2}$

(c) $10 + 4x = 6$
$(-10) \ (-10)$
$4x = -4$
$(\div 4) \ (\div 4)$
$x = -1$

(d) $6 = 14 - x$
$(+x) \ (+x)$
$6 + x = 14$
$(-6) \ (-6)$
$x = 8$

Note: Always make the x term positive.

Exercise 1

Solve the equations

1. $3x - 2 = 13$
2. $5x + 2 = 12$
3. $7x - 4 = 3$
4. $2x + 7 = 7$
5. $7 + 2x = 11$
6. $3 + 5x = 33$
7. $6 + 4x = 8$
8. $6x - 3 = 15$
9. $2x - 11 = 10$
10. $8x - 9 = 15$
11. $8 + 3x = 5$
12. $4x + 1 = 2$

Questions **13** to **24** are more difficult.

13. $3x - 2 = 0$
14. $4x + 1 = 25$
15. $7x - 2 = -1$
16. $5 + 2x = 6$
17. $7 + 3x = 22$
18. $3 = 4x + 1$
19. $5 = 3x - 1$
20. $7 = 15 - 2x$
21. $10 = 12 - 3x$
22. $4 = 6x + 5$
23. $7x - 1 = -8$
24. $3 - x = 10$

Equations with the unknown on both sides

(a) $3x = 2x + 7$

$(-2x)$ $(-2x)$ ← Removes the x term from R.H.S.

$x = 7$

(b) $5x = 14 - 2x$

$(+2x)$ $(+2x)$ ← Removes the x term from R.H.S.

$7x = 14$

$(\div 7)$ $(\div 7)$

$x = 2$

(c) $3x + 5 = 2x + 7$

$(-2x)$ $(-2x)$

$x + 5 = 7$

(-5) (-5)

$x = 2$

(d) $4x + 3 = 13 - x$

$(+x)$ $(+x)$

$5x + 3 = 13$

(-3) (-3)

$5x = 10$

$(\div 5)$ $(\div 5)$

$x = 2$

Exercise 2

Solve the equations

1. $4x = 2x + 6$
2. $7x = 4x + 12$
3. $2x = x + 17$
4. $4x = 3x + 11$
5. $3x - 5 = 2x$
6. $6x - 4 = 4x$
7. $5x - 8 = 3x$
8. $9x = 10 - x$
9. $6x = 24 - 2x$
10. $9x = 18 + 3x$
11. $2x = 15 - 3x$
12. $9x - 1 = 6x$

In Questions **13** to **24**, begin by putting the x terms on one side of the equation.

13. $4x + 3 = 2x + 5$
14. $7x - 5 = 2x + 10$
15. $3x + 7 = 8x + 2$
16. $6x + 1 = 2 - 3x$
17. $7x - 2 = 1 - 3x$
18. $5 - x = 2x - 7$
19. $5x - 8 = x + 12$
20. $3x - 9 = 4x + 4$
21. $2 + 8x = 5 - x$
22. $16x + 9 = 12x - 3$
23. $1 - 10x = 6 - 5x$
24. $4 - 5x = 4 + 7x$

Equations with brackets

Many of the more difficult problems which appear later in this section involve forming equations with brackets. Once the brackets have been removed the method of solution is similar to that for the equations dealt with earlier.

(a) $3(2x - 1) = 2(5 - x)$
$6x - 3 = 10 - 2x$
$6x + 2x = 10 + 3$
$8x = 13$
$x = 1\frac{5}{8}$

(b) $2(3x - 1) - (x - 2) = 5$
$6x - 2 - x + 2 = 5$
$5x = 5$
$x = 1$

Exercise 3

Solve the equations.

1. $3(x + 2) = 18$

2. $5(x - 2) = 10$

3. $4(x + 1) = 5$

4. $4(x + 4) = 20$

5. $3(2x + 1) = 9$

6. $2(3x - 1) = 10$

7. $4(x - 3) = 2x + 6$

8. $2(3x + 1) = 5x + 7$

9. $7(x - 4) = 3x$

10. $5 = 2(5 - x)$

11. $21 = 3(2x + 5)$

12. $8 = 4(5x - 1)$

Questions **13** to **24** involve two pairs of brackets

13. $3(x + 4) = 2(x + 5)$

14. $7(x + 2) = 4(x + 6)$

15. $6(x - 4) = 2(x - 1)$

16. $3(x + 5) = 2(4 - x)$

17. $4(1 - 3x) = 9(3 + x)$

18. $7(2x + 1) = 2(5 + 4x)$

19. $8(x - 3) = 2x$

20. $2(x + 1) + x = 7$

21. $7(x - 2) - 3 = 2(1 - x)$

22. $5(x - 1) - (x + 2) = 0$

23. $2(3x - 1) - 3(x + 1) = 0$

24. $4(x + 1) + 2(1 - x) = x$

Exercise 4

Solve the equations for x.

1. $3(x - 1) = 2x - 2$

2. $4(x + 2) = 3x + 10$

3. $2(2x - 1) = x + 4$

4. $3(x - 1) = 2(x + 1) - 2$

5. $4(2x - 1) = 3(x + 1) - 2$

6. $5 + 2(x + 1) = 5(x - 1)$

7. $6 + 3(x + 2) = 2(x + 5) + 4$

8. $5(x + 1) = 2x + 3 + x$

9. $4(2x - 2) = 5x - 17$

10. $x + 2(x + 4) = -4$

11. $3x + 2(x + 1) = 3x + 12$

12. $4x - 2(x + 4) = x + 1$

Questions **13** to **24** involve different unknowns.

13. $5(2a + 1) - 5 = 3(a + 1)$

14. $3(4a - 1) - 3 = a + 1$

15. $2(a - 10) = 4 - 3a$

16. $7(n - 3) = 10 - n$

17. $3(n + 1) = 2(n + 3) - 6$

18. $5(2n - 1) = 9(n + 1) - 8$

19. $3(t + 2) = 4(1 - t)$

20. $7(t + 3) = 2(3 - t)$

21. $3(2t + 1) = 4(5 - t)$

22. $5(y + 1) = 3(y - 2) + 12$

23. $3(y + 7) = 2(y + 1) + 20$

24. $2(2y - 1) = 3(1 - 2y)$

Using equations to solve problems

Many mathematical problems are easier to solve when an equation is formed. In general it is a good idea to start by introducing a letter like 'x' or 'h' to stand for the unknown quantity.

Philip is thinking of a number. He tells us that when he doubles it and adds 7, the answer is 18. What number is Philip thinking of?

Suppose that Philip is thinking of the number x

He tells us that	$2x + 7 = 18$
Subtract 7 from both sides:	$2x = 11$
Divide both sides by 2	$x = \frac{11}{2}$
	$x = 5\frac{1}{2}$

So Philip is thinking of the number $5\frac{1}{2}$

Exercise 5

In each question I am thinking of a number. Use the information to form an equation and then solve it to find the number.

1. If we multiply the number by 3 and then add 2, the answer is 13.

2. If we multiply the number by 5 and then subtract 3, the answer is 9.

3. If we multiply the number by 6 and then add 11, the answer is 16.

4. If we multiply the number by 11 and then subtract 4, the answer is 7.

5. If we double the number and add 10, the answer is 30.

6. If we multiply the number by 10 and then subtract 4, the answer we get is the same as when we multiply the number by 7 and then add 2.

7. If we multiply the number by 6 and subtract 1, the answer we get is the same as when we multiply the number by 2 and add 5.

8. If we multiply the number by 7 and add 3, the answer we get is the same as when we multiply the number by 2 and add 5.

9. If we treble the number and add 10, we get the same answer as when we multiply the number by 9 and add 8.

10. If we double the number and subtract *from* 7 we get the same answer as when we treble the number and add 2.

11. If we treble the number and subtract from 8 we get the same answer as when we double the number and add 7.

12. If we double the number, subtract 11 and then add the original number we get the same answer as when we subtract the number *from* 9.

Steven is thinking of a number. When he doubles the number, adds 4 and then multiplies the result by 3, the answer is 13. What number is he thinking of?

Let the number he is thinking of be x.
He doubles it, adds 4, multiplies the result by 3.
We have, $3(2x + 4) = 13$
$$6x + 12 = 13$$
$$6x = 1$$
$$x = \tfrac{1}{6}$$
Steven is thinking of the number $\tfrac{1}{6}$.

Exercise 6

In each question, I am thinking of a number. Use the information to form an equation and then solve it to find the number.

1. If I subtract 2 from the number and then multiply the result by 5, the answer is 11.

2. If I double the number and then subtract 7, the answer is 4.

3. If I multiply the number by 4, add 3 and then double the result, the answer is −2.

4. If I treble the number, add 2 and then double the result, the answer is 9.

5. If I add 4 to the number and then multiply the result by 7, I get the same answer as when I subtract 1 from the number and then double the result.

6. If I multiply the number by 7 and subtract 10, I get the same answer as when I add 2 to the number and then double the result.

7. If I multiply the number 5, subtract 2, and then multiply the result by 4, the answer I get is the same as when I double the number and then subtract 3.

8. If I double the number, add 3 and then multiply the result by 5, I get the same answer as when I double the number and then add 21.

Harder problems

The diagram shows a square.
Find the length of each side of the square
and hence find the area of the square.

A square has equal sides.
So:
$$5x - 8 = 3x + 2$$
$$5x - 3x = 2 + 8$$
$$2x = 10$$
$$x = 5$$

The side of the square is $3x + 2$
With $x = 5$, $3x + 2 = 17$
∴ The side of the square = 17 units

Finally the area of the square $= 17 \times 17$
$$= 289 \text{ square units.}$$

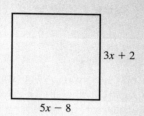

Exercise 7

1. The diagram shows a rectangle. Write an equation and solve it to find x.

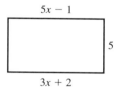

2. The length of a rectangle is three times its width. If the perimeter of the rectangle is 20 cm, find its width. [Hint: Let the width be x cm]

3. The length of a rectangle is 3 cm more than its width. If the perimeter of the rectangle is 30 cm, find its width.

4. In a quadrilateral ABCD, BC is twice as long as AB and AD is three times as long as AB. Side DC is 10 cm long. The perimeter of ABCD is 31 cm. Write an equation and solve it to find the length of AB.

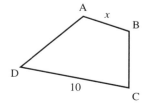

64

5. (a) Find x if perimeter is 18 cm.

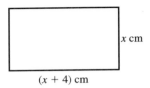

x cm

$(x + 4)$ cm

(b) Find x if the area is 6 cm^2.

5 cm

$(x - 4)$ cm

6. Sally has 5 times as many sweets as her brother Paul, but, as she is feeling generous, she gives him 10 of hers so that they now each have the same number. How many did Paul have originally? [Let the number that Paul had be x.]

7. The diagram shows two angles in an isosceles triangle. Find the angles in the triangle.

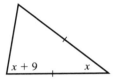

$x + 9$ x

8. In the quadrilateral:
AB $= x$ cm,
BC is 2 cm less than AB,
CD is twice as long as BC,
AD is 1 cm longer than CD.
If the perimeter of the quadrilateral is 33 cm, find the length of AB.

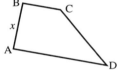

9. The total distance from P to T is 181 km.

The distance from Q to R is twice the distance from S to T.

R is mid-way between Q and S. The distance from P to Q is 5 km less than the distance from S to T.

Find the distance from S to T.

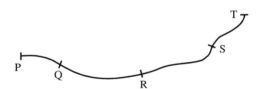

10. The angles of a triangle are A, B and C. Angle B is twice as big as angle A and angle C is 10° bigger than angle A.
Find the size of angle A.

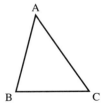

2.5 Mental arithmetic

Reminder of some basic methods

A	'Easy to add' numbers	$18 + 57 + 32 = 50 + 57 = 107$
B	Splitting numbers	$46 + 37 = 40 + 30 + 6 + 7 = 70 + 13 = 83$
C	Add/subtract with adjustment	$57 + 19 = 57 + 20 - 1 = 76$
D	Doubling from the left	double $78 =$ double $70 +$ double $8 = 156$
E	Multiply by 50, 25	$44 \times 25 = 44 \times 100 \div 4 = 1100$
F	Multiply by 19, 29 … 21, 31, …	$15 \times 21 = 15 \times 20 + 15 = 315$

The questions in the tests below should be read out by a teacher and you should not be looking at them. Each question should be repeated once and then the answer, and only the answer, should be written down.

Test 1

1. What are two eighteens?

2. Add together 7, 8 and 9.

3. Divide 8 into 40.

4. Multiply 15 by 3.

5. Write $\frac{3}{4}$ as a percentage.

6. Work out 13 divided by 10 as a decimal.

7. What number is 40 less than 120?

8. Share a cost of £60 between 4 people.

9. What four coins make 67p?

10. What is the product of 60 and 3?

11. I have 2 dogs and 3 cats. What fraction of my pets are dogs?

12. What is the cost of 2 C.D.s at £5·99 each?

13. Subtract the sum of 7 and 8 from 30.

14. One quarter of a number is 3·5. What is the number?

15. I have one 10p, three 5p and one 50p coin. How much money do I have?

16. What number is half way between 4·2 and 4·8?

17. Apples cost 75p for five. What is the cost of one apple?

18. A bunch of grapes costs 64p. What is the change from £1?

19. How many 20p coins do I need for £1·60?

20. A shirt costs £21·95 new. I get a discount of £4. How much do I pay?

21. I share 60 sweets equally among 5 people. How many sweets does each receive?

22. The area of a square is $36 \, cm^2$. How long is each side?

23. Write the number forty thousand and four in figures.

24. How many millimetres are there in 10 metres?

Test 2

1. Add together 15, 25 and 70.

2. How many millimetres are there in a kilometre?

3. Find the length of the perimeter of a regular hexagon of side 20 cm.

4. Find the change from £10 when you buy two magazines for 75p each.

5. Give a rough estimate for the square root of 150.

6. Find the cost of 60 eggs at £1 per dozen.

7. A car is travelling at a steady speed of 30 m.p.h. How far does it go in 30 minutes?

8. Find the difference between $8\frac{1}{2}$ and 20.

9. Work out $1 + 2^2 + 3^3$.

10. Through what angle does the minute hand of a clock move between 8·50 and 9·30?

11. Work out roughly the area of a circle of radius 10 cm.

12. A bridge was built in Paris in 1780. How many years ago was that?

13. What is 40% as a fraction?

14. How many items costing £25 each can you buy with £200?

15. What five coins make 75p?

16. Calculate the length of the perimeter of a rectangular field measuring 110 m by 80 m.

17. Work out 0·03 multiplied by 1000.

18. Increase a price of £700 by 1%.

19. Answer true or false: $\left(\frac{1}{3}\right)^2$ is greater than $\frac{1}{3}$.

20. A large brick weighs 1 kg. Roughly what does it weigh in pounds?

21. Work out 1% of £150.

22. A plant grows 5 cm every day. How many days will it take to grow 60 cm?

23. A charity collection is made into a pile of 1000 20p coins. How much was collected?

24. Add together 67 and 77.

25. True or false: At a steady speed of 30 m.p.h. you go 1 mile every 2 minutes.

26. Glen has one of each of the coins from 1 p to 1 pound. What is their total value?

27. Three angles of a quadrilateral are 80°, 120° and 60°. What is the fourth angle?

28. How many inches are there in a foot?

29. A pie chart has a pink sector representing 25% of the whole chart. What is the angle of the sector?

30. Write down the next prime number after 31.

Test 3

1. Which of these fractions is the larger: $\frac{2}{3}$ or $\frac{3}{4}$?

2. True or false: a weight of 5 stones is less than 50 kg.

3. Work out 1% of £45.

4. Write in words the answer to $10 \times 100 \times 1000$.

5. Add together 5, 6, 7 and 8.

6. A car travels 30 miles in 30 minutes. How far will it travel at this speed in $\frac{3}{4}$ hour?

7. Sam spends 40% of his money on tapes and 50% of his money on clothes. If he had £5 left, how much did he have at first?

8. Write as a decimal: $\frac{1}{5}$ plus $\frac{1}{10}$.

9. A bucket contains 2 litres of milk. How much is left, in ml, after 100 ml is removed?

10. How many hours and minutes is it from 8·15 a.m. until noon?

11. One bag weighs 250 g. How many bags weigh 5 kg?

12. If 20 drinks cost £28, find the cost of 5.

13. A magazine costing 47p was paid for with a £1 coin. Which three coins were given as change?

14. What is the number which is 200 less than 2000?

15. Find the change from a £5 note after buying 3 pounds of apples at 20p per pound.

16. A girl faces West and turns clockwise through 1 right angle. In which direction is she now facing?

17. A film, lasting $1\frac{1}{2}$ hours, starts at 6·20. When does it finish?

18. Work out $100 - 4·9$.

19. Name the date which is 4 months before the 1st of February.

20. Write down the next prime number after 20.

21. Write $\frac{9}{10}$ as a percentage.

22. Of the people in a room, a half were French, ten per cent were German and the rest were Irish. What percentage were Irish?

23. In January, Steve weighs 70 kg. By July his weight is reduced by 10%. What does he weigh in July?

24. Find the total surface area of a cube of side 1 cm.

25. Work out $98 + 67$.

26. Write 1·6 recurring correct to one decimal place.

27. A 10p coin is 1·7 mm thick. What is the height, in cm, of a pile of coins worth £1?

28. Estimate the length of a side of a square of area 50 cm².

29. Work out $\frac{2}{3}$ of £120.

30. True or false: 15 cm is about 6 inches.

Test 4

1. If I have 35 pence change from a ten pound note, how much have I spent?

2. My train leaves at 16·18. How many minutes do I have to wait if I arrive at the station at 15·55?

3. The area of a triangle is 20 cm². Its base measures 10 cm. What is the height of the triangle?

4. One eighth of the children in a class walk to school. What percentage of the class is this?

5. A man was born in 1939. How old was he in 2000?

6. A piece of string 54 cm long is cut into four equal parts. How long is each part?

7. True or false: Five miles is about the same as eight km.

8. The time in Miami is 5 hours earlier than the time in England. If I want to telephone Miami at 13·30 their time, what time will it be here?

9. I think of a number, multiply it by 2 and subtract 8. The result is 12. What number am I thinking of?

10. A plank of wood measures 2 metres by 50 cm. What is the area of the plank in square metres?

11. Which is largest: $\frac{1}{9}$ or 10%?

12. A bar of chocolate costs 18p. I buy as many as I can for 50p. How much change will I receive?

13. Add together 1, 2, 3, 4, 5, 6.

14. Write down ten million millimetres in kilometres.

15. By how much does a half of 130 exceed 49?

16. Work out two squared plus three squared.

17. Work out 5% of £40.

18. Two angles in a quadrilateral are each 80° and a third angle is 100°. What is the fourth angle?

19. Give an *estimate* for $291·4 \times 0·486$.

20. What number is a quarter of 140?

21. What is a half of a half of £60?

22. Rosie is going on a 2 week holiday. She leaves on the 5th of July. On what date will she return?

23. What is 2% as a simplified fraction?

24. What is the fraction exactly half way between $\frac{1}{4}$ and $\frac{1}{2}$?

For the last six questions you may write down the numbers in the question.

25. Work out 15% of £60.

26. I think of a number, subtract 8 and then divide by 2. The result is 1. What number am I thinking of?

27. My newspaper costs 45p per day from Monday to Friday and 50p on Saturday. How much do I spend on papers from Monday to Saturday?

28. The coordinates of the 4 corners of a rectangle are (1, 1), (5, 1), (5, 4) and (1, 4). What is the area of the rectangle in square units?

29. How many seconds are there in 1 hour?

30. A train journey of 480 miles took 4 hours. What was the average speed of the train?

Test 5

1. How many 20 pence coins are needed to make £8?

2. What number is mid-way between 0·1 and 0·2?

3. Work out 5% of £320.

4. True or false: one yard is approximately one metre.

5. Work out 2·2 divided by ten.

6. One sector of a pie chart represents 10% of the whole chart. What is the angle of the sector?

7. Find the approximate area of a circle of diameter 6 cm.

8. I pay for a pen costing £3.40 with a £20 note. What change do I receive?

9. Who is taller: Jan who is 5 feet tall or Sam who is 1 metre 10 tall?

10. A jar contains 1000 5p coins. Find the total value of the coins.

11. A rectangle measures 2·4 m by 10 cm. What is its perimeter in cm?

12. A rope of length 1 foot 4 inches is cut in half. How long is each piece?

13. A film started at 7·10 and finished at 10·55. How long was the film in hours and minutes?

14. Which has the longer perimeter: a square of side 10 cm or a circle of diameter 10 cm?

15. What fraction is equivalent to 40%?

16. Find the cost of 4 litres of wine at £1·25 per litre.

17. How many 24p stamps can be bought for £3?

18. Add together 34 and 164.

19. How long will it take to travel 60 miles at a speed of 30 m.p.h.?

20. Work out $3 \times 30 \times 30$.

21. What is the angle between the hands of a clock at 4 o'clock?

22. Find the cost of buying a newspaper for 40 days if each paper costs 45p.

23. Work out two fifths of £40.

24. How many prime numbers are there between 10 and 20?

25. I am thinking of a number. If I double it, add one and then square the result the answer is 25. What number am I thinking of?

26. Work out $\frac{1}{4}$ plus $\frac{1}{2}$ and give the answer as a decimal.

27. Divide one million by 100.

28. A rectangle has area 12 cm². What is the area of a rectangle whose sides are twice as long as those of this rectangle?

29. In a quiz, David got 15 out of 20. What percentage is that?

30. Increase a price of £300 by 10%.

The next 2 tests are written in the form of the Key Stage 3 mental arithmetic tests.

Each question will be repeated once. You have 5 seconds to answer questions 1 to 6, 10 seconds to answer questions 7 to 20 and 15 seconds to answer the remaining questions. You will be told to put down your pen after the correct time interval for each question.

Work out the answer to each question in your head and write down only the answer. Sometimes other useful information, such as the numbers used in the question, has been written down to help you. Look at the sheets on page 72.

Test 1

● Time: 5 seconds

  1. Look at the numbers on your answer sheet. What is half their total?

  2. Change one hundred and ninety millimetres into centimetres.

  3. What is seventy-two divided by eight?

  4. Look at the equation. Write down the value for x.

  5. Your answer sheet shows a fraction. Write the fraction in its simplest form.

  6. Write two fifths as a decimal number.

● Time: 10 seconds

  7. What is half of two hundred and thirty-six?

  8. A TV film starts at five minutes to ten. It lasts forty-five minutes. At what time does the film finish?

  9. Write all the prime numbers between ten and twenty.

  10. On a coach there are 45 pupils. 20 of the pupils are boys. A pupil is chosen at random. What is the probability that a boy is chosen?

  11. Look at your answer sheet. Work out the answer.

  12. One per cent of a number is six. What is the number?

  13. A path is six feet wide. About how many metres is that?

  14. Write the number two and a half million in figures.

  15. Look at the equation. Use it to work out the value of x plus 2.

  16. On your sheet is a scale. Estimate the number shown by the arrow.

  17. Estimate the value of forty-eight per cent of eighteen pounds twenty pence.

  18. A book costs two pounds ninety-five pence. How much change is there from ten pounds?

  19. What is two thousand minus one hundred and fifty?

  20 n stands for a number. Write an expression for the following: 'add four to n, then multiply the result by five'.

- Time: 15 seconds

21. Forty pounds is shared in the ratio of one to three. How much money is the smaller share?

22. What is one eighth of four hundred?

23. Look at the equation on your answer sheet. If n equals two, what is h?

24. Use the calculation on your answer sheet to help you to work out how many fifteens there are in one thousand eight hundred.

25. Divide twenty-two pounds between four people. How much money does each person get?

26. Write an approximate answer to the calculation on your answer sheet.

27. A square has a perimeter of twenty metres. What is the area of the square?

28. Your answer sheet shows the marks by five pupils in a test. What is the mean mark?

29. Look at the expression on your answer sheet. Write down a value of x which makes the value of the expression zero.

30. On the answer sheet find the missing number.

Test 2

- Time: 5 seconds

1. Change four and a half metres into centimetres.

2. What is three point seven multiplied by one thousand?

3. Work out twenty-five per cent of two hundred.

4. Simplify the expression on your answer sheet as fully as possible.

5. What is the sum of the numbers on your answer sheet?

6. What is one tenth of one million?

- Time: 10 seconds

7. Look at the expression. What is its value when x equals five?

8. A roll of wallpaper is six metres long. How many one point five metre lengths can be cut?

9. Five per cent of a number is eight. What is the number?

10. Two angles in a triangle are each thirty-five degrees. What is the size of the third angle?

11. In a group of seventy-five children, twenty-six are girls. How many are boys?

12. What is the area of this triangle?

13. The value of three x plus two y. Write the value of six x plus two y.

14. Look at the equation. Use it to work out the value of $2n$.

15. Mandy got thirty out of fifty on a test. What percentage did she get?

16. Multiply nought point two by thirty.

17. Look at the inequalities on your answer sheet. Write down one possible value for x.

18 Work out two plus four plus six all squared.

19. Multiply five point nought seven by one thousand.

20. On the answer sheet find the missing number.

- Time: 15 seconds:

21. What is the cost of three items at ninety-nine pence each?

22. Look at these numbers. Put a ring around the smallest number.

23. Write an approximate answer to the calculation on your answer sheet.

24. Each side of a square is fifty-five centimetres. What is the perimeter of the square?

25. Look at the calculation on your answer sheet. What is three hundred and twenty multiplied by one hundred and fifty?

26. Look at the sequence on your answer sheet. Write down the next two terms.

27. A map has a scale of one to one thousand. What is the actual length of a path which is five cm long on the map?

28. Look at the expression on your answer sheet. Write down the value of the expression when x equals one.

29. Work out a quarter plus a tenth and give the answer as a decimal.

30. Find the approximate area of a circle of radius 10 cm.

72

Test 1 Answer sheet

Time: 5 seconds

Question	Answer	
1		37 53
2	cm	
3		
4		$x^2 = 49$
5		$\frac{18}{24}$
6		

Time: 10 seconds

7		
8		
9		10 20
10		45 pupils, 20 boys
11		$25 - (7{\cdot}2 + 0{\cdot}8)$
12		
13	m	
14		
15		$x - 11 = 20$
16		
17		48% £18·20
18		£2·95
19		
20		

Time: 15 seconds

21	£	1:3 £40
22		
23	$h =$	$h = 12n - 10$
24		$15 \times 240 = 3600$, 1800
25		
26		$\dfrac{81{\cdot}6 \times 4{\cdot}17}{2{\cdot}09}$
27	m^2	
28		1, 4, 5, 5, 15
29		$(x - 3)(x + 4)$
30		$2 \times \square + 10 = 60$

Test 2 Answer sheet

Time: 5 seconds

Question	Answer	
1	cm	$4\frac{1}{2}\,\text{m}$
2		3·7
3		
4		$3a + b - a + 3b$
5		2·2 4·8 2
6		

Time: 10 seconds

7		$2(x + 1)$
8		1·5 m 6 m
9		
10		
11		
12	cm^2	
13		$3x + y = 15$, $6x + 2y$
14		$n + 5 = 13$
15	%	
16		
17		$-3 < x < 2$
18		$(2 + 4 + 6)^2$
19		5·07
20		$5 \times \square - 2 = 28$

Time: 15 seconds

21	£	
22		0·0101 $\frac{1}{100}$ 0·011 0·099
23		$405{\cdot}7 \div 19{\cdot}3$
24	cm	
25		$32 \times 15 = 480$
26	,	3, 6, 12, 24
27	m	1 : 1000 5 cm
28		$2 \times (x + 2)$
29		$\frac{1}{4}$ $\frac{1}{10}$
30	cm^2	radius 10 cm

2.6 Mixed problems 1

Exercise 1

1. Copy and complete the following bill.

$5\frac{1}{2}$ kg of carrots at 64p per kg = £

2 kg of meat at   per kg = £9·70

jars of marmalade at 85p per jar = £5·95

Total = £

2. A ship's voyage started at 20.30 on Monday and finished at 07.00 on the following Wednesday. How long was the journey in hours and minutes?

3. Twenty articles cost £50. How many of these articles could be bought for £7·50?

4. A man starts work each day at 07.30 and works until 16.00. He stops working for one hour at lunchtime. How many hours does he work in a 5-day week?

5. Copy each pattern and write down the next line

(a) $2^2 = 1^2 + 3$
$3^2 = 2^2 + 5$
$4^2 = 3^2 + 7$
$5^2 = 4^2 + 9$

(b) $1 + 9 \times 0 = 1$
$2 + 9 \times 1 = 11$
$3 + 9 \times 12 = 111$
$4 + 9 \times 123 = 1111$

6. How many 10 mm pieces of wire can be cut from a wire of length 1 metre?

7. Find the number indicated by the arrow on the scales below.

(a)
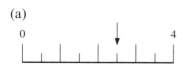

(b)

(c)
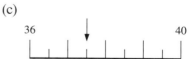

(d)
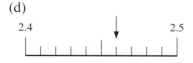

(e)

(f)
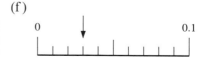

8. A woman hires a car from a car hire firm which charges £15 per day plus 7p per km travelled.

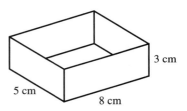

   £15 per day
   7p per km

   (a) How much does it cost to hire a car for four days and drive 200 km?
   (b) How much does it cost to hire a car for six days and drive 650 km?
   (c) A woman hired a car for two days and had to pay £65. How far did she drive?

Exercise 2

1. A packet of baby food makes 200 feeds. A baby has 5 feeds a day. How many days will the packet last?

2. John is 12 years old and his father is 31 years older than he is. John's mother is 3 years younger than his father. How old is John's mother?

3. The number in each square is the product of the two numbers in circles on either side of it. Copy and complete.

(a)   (b)

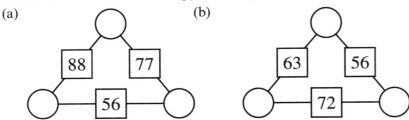

4. When a car journey starts, the mileometer reads 42 714 miles. After two hours the mileometer reads 42 858 miles. What is the average speed of the car?

5. Change the following 12-hour clock times to 24-hour clock times
   (a) 7.30 a.m.
   (b) 7.30 p.m.
   (c) 1.00 p.m.

6. How many apples costing 8p each can be bought with £1?

7. How many cubes, each of edge 1 cm, are required to fill a box with internal dimensions 5 cm by 8 cm by 3 cm?

3 cm

5 cm

8 cm

8. In a 'magic' square the sum of the numbers in any row, column or main diagonal is the same. Copy and complete these magic squares.

(a)

6		2
	5	
		4

(b)

3	6	10	
16	9		4
	12	8	
	7		

9. A wall measuring 3 m by 2 m is to be covered with square tiles of side 10 cm.
(a) How many tiles are needed?
(b) If the tiles cost £3·40 for ten, how much will it cost?

10. A journey by helicopter takes 3 hours 35 minutes.
How long will it take at half the speed?

Exercise 3

1. Use a calculator to work out, correct to 1 decimal place

(a) $19·6 - 6·2 \times 2·13$

(b) $\dfrac{18·7}{5·6 - 2·91}$

(c) $\left(\dfrac{8·2 + 1·173}{7·59}\right)^2$

2. Here is a number machine

Fill in the spaces to find the numbers which come out of each box.

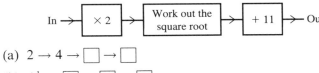

(a) $2 \rightarrow 4 \rightarrow \square \rightarrow \square$

(b) $4\frac{1}{2} \rightarrow \square \rightarrow \square \rightarrow \square$

(c) $32 \rightarrow \square \rightarrow \square \rightarrow \square$

3. Steve is putting tennis balls into boxes.
Six balls go in each box and he has
76 balls.
How many full boxes will he have
and how many balls will be left over?

4. For an advertising photo, men were asked to bring their children and to stand 3 yards apart next to a road of length 10 miles. How many men were needed? [1 mile = 1760 yards]

5. Here is a row of numbers

1 2 3 4 5 6 7 8 9 10 11 12 13 14 15 16 17

(a) Find *two* numbers next to each other which add up to 25.
(b) Find *three* numbers next to each other which add up to 45.
(c) Find *four* numbers next to each other which add up to 38.

6. (a) Sarita puts a 2 digit whole number into her calculator. She multiplies the number by 10.

(b) Sarita starts again with the same 2 digit number and this time she multiplies it by 100. Fill in all four digits on the calculator this time.

7. How many apples at 16p each would be a fair exchange for 48 oranges costing 11p each?

8. A jar with 7 chocolates in it weighs 130 g. The same jar with 15 chocolates in it weighs 210 g. How much does the jar weigh on its own?

9. Copy and complete the additions.

(a)

```
    8 2 □
    2 □ 1
+   □ 3 2
  ─────────
  □ 2 9 8
```

(b)

```
    7 3 □
    3 □ 5
+   □ 6 2
  ─────────
  □ 7 0 9
```

10. Use the clues to find the mystery number
- the sum of the digits is 18
- the number reads the same forwards as backwards
- the number is less than 2000
- the number has four digits

Exercise 4

1. A greengrocer sells 9 kg of carrots for £2·79.
Find:
(a) the cost of 1 kg,
(b) how many kg can be bought for £1·86.

2. Here is a subtraction using the digits
3, 4, 5, 6, 7.
Which subtraction using all the digits
3, 4, 5, 6, 7 has the smallest positive answer?

$$546 - 37$$

3. It costs 10p per minute to operate a machine. How much will it
cost to operate the machine from 12 50 to 14 15?

4. A pound coin has radius 1·1 cm and
thickness 3 mm.
Calculate the height of a pile of pound
coins of total value £1000.

5. A man is 22 cm taller than his daughter, who is 7 cm shorter
than her mother. The man was born in 1949 and is 1·80 m tall.
How tall is the wife?

6. Copy and complete the pattern below.

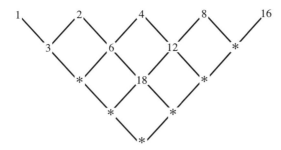

7. Two numbers *m* and *n* are such that *n* is greater than 9 and *m* is less than 4. Arrange the numbers 7, *m* and *n* in order of size, starting with the smallest.

8. Draw the next member of the sequence

(a)

(b)

(c)

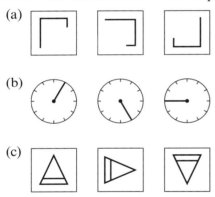

9. I think of a number. If I add 5 and then divide the result by 2 the answer is 8. What number was I thinking of?

10. A car travels 10 km on a litre of petrol and petrol costs £0·74 per litre. Over a period of one year the car travels a distance of 6600 km. How much does the petrol cost for the whole year?

Part 3

4.1 Area

Rectangle

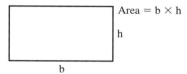

Area = b × h

Triangle

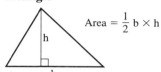

Area = $\frac{1}{2}$ b × h

Exercise 1

Find the area of each shape. All lengths are in cm.

1.

2.

3.

4.

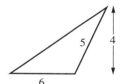

5.

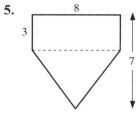

6.

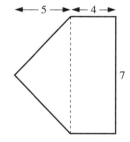

7.

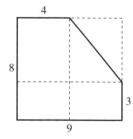

8.

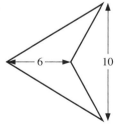

9. Find the shaded area.

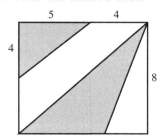

10. Find the shaded area.

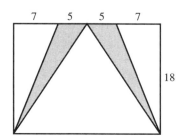

In Questions **11** to **14** the area is written inside the shape. Calculate
the length of the side marked x.

11.

12.

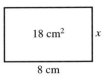

13.

14.

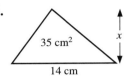

Trapezium and parallelogram

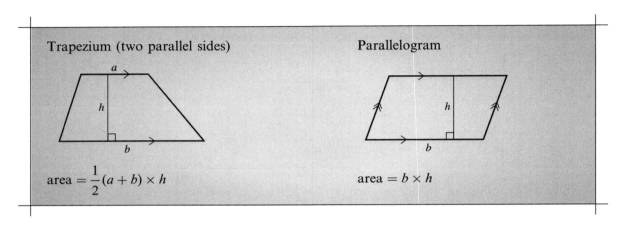

Trapezium (two parallel sides)

Parallelogram

area $= \dfrac{1}{2}(a+b) \times h$

area $= b \times h$

Exercise 2

Find the area of each shape. All lengths are in cm.

1.

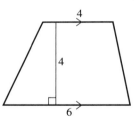

2.

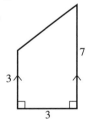

3.

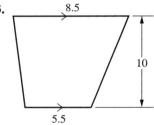

4.

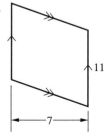

5.

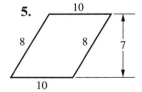

6.

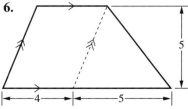

7. These two trapeziums are drawn carefully. Take measurements and then find the area of each one.

(a)
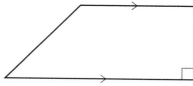

(b)
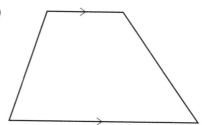

8. Find the area of the end of this shed.

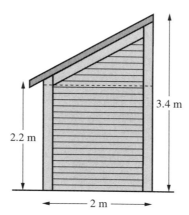

9. This is the side wall of a swimming pool. Find its area.

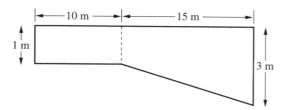

10. Here are the plans of two rooms in which all the lengths are in metres. Find the area of each room.

(a)
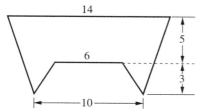

(b)
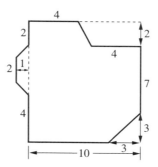

Mixed area problems

Exercise 3

1. The diagram shows a picture 20 cm by 15 cm surrounded by a border 5 cm wide. What is the area of the border?

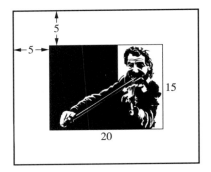

2. A rectangular lawn 17 m by 8 m is surrounded by a path 1 m wide. What is the area of the path?

3. A wall measuring 5 m by 3·5 m is to be covered by square tiles measuring 50 cm by 50 cm. How many tiles are needed?

4. A rectangular area 3 m by 1·2 m is to be covered by paving slabs measuring 50 cm by 40 cm. What is the least number of slabs needed?

5. How many panes of glass 35 cm by 10 cm can be cut from a sheet 105 cm by 110 cm?

6. A flag has a sloping strip drawn across. Calculate the area of the shaded strip.

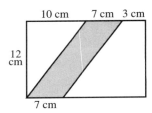

7. A rectangle has a perimeter of 28 m and a length of 6·5 m. What is its area?

8. The field shown is sold at £3250 per acre. Calculate the price paid. [1 acre = 4840 square yards]

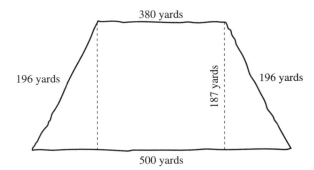

9. A groundsman has enough grass seed to cover three hectares. [1 hectare = 10 000 m²]. A tennis court measures 15 m by 40 m. How many courts can he cover with seed?

10. A rectangular field 350 m long has an area of 7 hectares. Calculate the perimeter of the field.

11. A waterproofing spray is applied to the outside of the 4 walls, including the door, and the roof of the garage shown.
   (a) Calculate the total area to be sprayed.
   (b) The spray comes in cans costing £1·95 and each can is enough to cover 4 m². How much will it cost to spray this garage? [Assume you have to buy full cans].

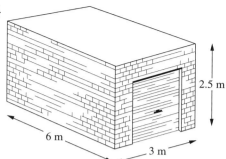

12.

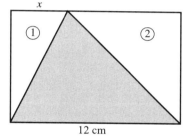

A gardener is using moss killer on his lawn. The instructions say that 4 measures of the mosskiller, in water, will treat 10 m² of lawn. The box contains 250 measures and costs £12·50.
Find the area of the lawn and hence the cost of the moss killer required.

13. The shaded triangle is drawn inside a rectangle with longer side 12 cm.
   (a) If area of triangle ② = 2 × (area of triangle ①), find the length x.
   (b) If area of triangle ② = 3 × (area of triangle ①), find the length x.

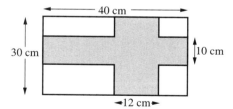

14. Here is a flag.
Calculate the area of the shaded cross.

15. The area is written inside the triangle. Calculate x.
   (a)   (b)

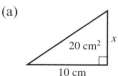
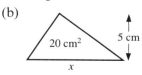

16.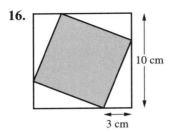

3 cm

10 cm

The diagram shows a shaded square inside a larger square.
Calculate the area of the shaded square.

3.2 Estimating

- In some situations an estimate of a quantity is more helpful than the actual number. For example we may know that on January 1st 1996 the population of France is 61 278 514 and the population of Greece is 9 815 972. For purposes of comparison we could use 60 million for France and 10 million for Greece so that the population of France is *about* six times that of Greece.

- Find an estimate for the area of a circular pond of radius 10·8 m.

We know that area $= \pi \times (\text{radius})^2$.

The value of π is about 3 and the radius is about 10 m.

So area $\approx 3 \times 10^2$

The area of the pond is about 300 m^2.

- Estimate the following.

  (a) $\dfrac{58 \cdot 2 \times 28 \cdot 4}{18 \cdot 27} \approx \dfrac{6\cancel{0} \times 30}{2\cancel{0}} \approx 90$

  (b) $\dfrac{42 \cdot 3 + 56 \cdot 1}{2 \cdot 14} \approx \dfrac{40 + 60}{2} \approx 50$

  (c) 48% of £22 615 $\approx \dfrac{50}{1\cancel{00}} \times 20\,0\cancel{00} \approx £10\,000$

Exercise 1

Do not use a calculator. Decide, by estimating, which of the three answers is closest to the exact value. Write the letter A, B or C for each part.

	Calculation	A	B	C
1.	$98 \cdot 4 \times 11 \cdot 1$	100	90	1000
2.	$6 \cdot 83 \times 9 \cdot 74$	30	70	700
3.	$18 \cdot 9 \times 21 \cdot 8$	200	400	4000
4.	$5 \cdot 1 \times 9 \cdot 23$	4.9	99	49
5.	$1 \cdot 01 \times 80 \cdot 6$	8	80	0·8
6.	$6 \cdot 8 \times 11 \cdot 4$	80	44	600
7.	$18 \cdot 9 \times 21$	40	4000	400
8.	$2 \cdot 2 \times 96$	22	200	440
9.	$972 \times 21 \cdot 4$	10 000	2000	20 000
10.	$24\,723 \times 10 \cdot 37$	2·5 million	250 000	25 000
11.	$208 \cdot 4 \div 18 \cdot 9$	0·1	2	20
12.	$83 \cdot 75 \div 1 \cdot 18$	82	8·2	120
13.	$55 \cdot 14 \div 99 \cdot 6$	0·2	0·5	2
14.	$1211 \div 986 \cdot 4$	1·2	12	0·8
15.	$38 \cdot 4 \div 0 \cdot 96$	0·4	4	38
16.	$207 \times 2 \cdot 16$	4400	208	410
17.	$73 \cdot 4 \times 97 \cdot 4$	70 000	700	7000
18.	$1200 \times 0 \cdot 89$	120	1200	360
19.	$3 \cdot 2 \times 4 \cdot 2$	8·2	13·4	83·4
20.	$4 \cdot 01 \times 960$	3800	380	940
21.	$\dfrac{4 \cdot 2 + 98 \cdot 71}{1 \cdot 95}$	5	50	80
22.	$\dfrac{84 \cdot 3 - 2 \cdot 72}{41 \cdot 7}$	1·2	2·1	5·6
23.	$\dfrac{1 \cdot 85 \times 61 \cdot 4}{30 \cdot 6}$	0·4	4	20
24.	$9 \cdot 8\%$ of $122 \cdot 7$	12	120	1·2
25.	51% of 2613	560	130	1300
26.	$4 \cdot 12 + 594 \cdot 6$	5	600	2400
27.	$201 \cdot 8 - 0 \cdot 113$	0·7	50	200
28.	$0 \cdot 0714 + 92 \cdot 4$	90	0·4	900
29.	$\sqrt{25 \cdot 13} \times 6 \cdot 03$	15	30	150
30.	$22 \cdot 2 \times \sqrt{97 \cdot 6}$	2000	20	200

Exercise 2 (No calculators!)

1. Steve buys 52 cinema tickets at £4·95 each. Estimate the total cost.

2. One hundred and four people share the cost of hiring a coach. Roughly how much does each person pay if the total cost was £3118?

3. The total weight of 18 people in a lift was 1224 kg. Work out the approximate average (mean) weight of the people.

4. A Grand Prix racing car goes around each lap in about 1 minute 52·6 seconds. Roughly how many minutes will the car take to go 72 laps?

5. Tracy buys five articles at £1·99 each and 28 items at 21p each. Roughly how much does she spend altogether?

6. A pile of 19 sheets of card is 62 mm thick. Roughly how thick is each sheet of card?

7. A wedding cake weighing 9·2 kg is cut up and shared between 107 guests. About how much cake, in grams, does each person get?

8. The monthly rental for a video is £9·25. About how much is paid in rent over four years?

9. The total weight of 95 000 marbles is 308 kg. Roughly how many grams does each marble weigh?

In Questions **10** and **11** there are nine calculations and nine answers. Write down each calculation and choose the correct answer from the list given.

10. (a) $1·8 \times 10·4$ (b) $9·8 \times 9·1$ (c) $7·9 \times 8·1$
    (d) $76·2 \times 1·9$ (e) $3·8 \times 8·2$ (f) $8·15 \times 5·92$
    (g) $36·96 \div 4$ (h) $9·6 \div 5$ (i) $0·11 + 3·97$

    Answers: 63·99, 18·72, 31·16, 4·08, 1·92, 9·24, 144·78, 89·18, 48·248.

11. (a) $5·89 \times 10$ (b) $1·02 \div 10$ (c) $101·4 \div 5$
    (d) $7·2 \times 1·9$ (e) $4·3 \times 6·8$ (f) $3·57 \div 3$
    (g) $7·76 \div 2$ (h) 10% of 350   (i) $43·56 \div 6$

    Answers: 13·68, 7·26, 29·24, 3·88, 1·19, 20·28, 58·9, 0·102, 35·0.

12. In the numbers below the decimal point has been left out. Write out each line and put the decimal point in the right place.
   (a) length of a football pitch   9572 m
   (b) width of this book   1831 cm
   (c) height of the classroom door   205 m
   (d) weight of a box of Corn Flakes   5000 g
   (e) area of a postcard   1450 cm^2
   (f) price of 1000 four finger Kit Kats   £22 000

Multiplying and dividing by numbers between 0 and 1

When you multiply by a number greater than 1, you make it bigger

When you multiply by a number less than 1, you make it smaller

When you divide by a number greater than 1, you make it smaller

When you divide by a number less than 1, you make it bigger

E.g. $5 \cdot 7 \times 1 \cdot 2 > 5 \cdot 7$ E.g. $5 \cdot 7 \times 0 \cdot 8 < 5 \cdot 7$
E.g. $5 \cdot 7 \div 1 \cdot 2 < 5 \cdot 7$ E.g. $5 \cdot 7 \div 0 \cdot 8 > 5 \cdot 7$

Look at these calculations and decide whether the symbol in the box should be '>' or '<'.

$8 \cdot 5 \times 1 \cdot 18 \ \Box \ 8 \cdot 5$, $19 \cdot 4 \div 0 \cdot 3 \ \Box \ 19 \cdot 4$, $211 \div 1 \cdot 4 \ \Box \ 211$

Exercise 3

1. Write down each statement with either '>' or '<' in the box.

   (a) $4 \cdot 2 \times 0 \cdot 93 \ \Box \ 4 \cdot 2$ (b) $18 \cdot 6 \times 1 \cdot 75 \ \Box \ 18 \cdot 6$

   (c) $67 \div 0 \cdot 74 \ \Box \ 67$ (d) $5 \cdot 9 \times 0 \cdot 811 \ \Box \ 5 \cdot 9$

2. Write down each statement and next to it write 'true' or 'false'.
   (a) $3 \cdot 58 \times 1 \cdot 3 > 3 \cdot 58$ (b) $19 \times 0 \cdot 92 > 19$ (c) $5 \cdot 5 \times 1 \cdot 04 > 5 \cdot 5$
   (d) $9 \cdot 2 \div 1 \cdot 5 < 9 \cdot 2$ (e) $11 \cdot 2 \div 0 \cdot 87 > 11 \cdot 2$ (f) $67 \div 1 \cdot 34 < 67$
   (g) $59 \times 0 \cdot 89 < 59$ (h) $10 \cdot 42 \times 0 \cdot 73 < 10 \cdot 42$ (i) $17 \div 0 \cdot 99 > 17$
   (j) $0 \cdot 2^2 > 0 \cdot 2$ (k) $161 \div 0 \cdot 41 > 161$ (l) $(0 \cdot 85)^2 < 0 \cdot 85$

3. A doctor is paid a salary of £49 450 per year. Work out a rough estimate for her weekly pay.

4. Estimate the mean weight of articles with the following weights:
   4·9 kg,   0·21 kg,   0·72 kg,   25·1 kg,   0·11 kg.

5. In 1996 Helen's pay was £19 380 per year. In 1997 she receives a pay increase of 19·2%. Estimate the increase in Helen's pay.

6. Two people on a bike travel at an average speed of 98·7 km/h from 08.10 until 12.17. Roughly how far do they go?

7. Estimate the area of a circular pond of radius 7·1 m.

8. A lorry can carry a maximum load of 30 tonnes. A copy of Elmwood's Almanac weighs 475 g. The manager of the delivery firm estimates that each lorry can take about 6000 copies of the book. Is this a reasonable estimate? If not suggest a better estimate. [1 tonne = 1000 kg]

9. In the grounds of his palace, the Sultan of Brunei has a circular pond with a circumference of 61·5 m. Estimate the diameter of the pond in metres.

10. Estimate the mean weight, in kg, of two wrestlers weighing 131 kg and 72·4 kg respectively.

11. Give an estimate for each of the following calculations.

(a) $\dfrac{1·97 \times 19·6}{5·14}$

(b) $\dfrac{2848·7 - 1·94}{0·32 + 39·83}$

(c) 52% of 0·394 kg

(d) $\dfrac{3·15 + 30·63}{0·104}$

(e) $\frac{7}{15}$ of £3918·25

(f) $\dfrac{207·5 + 4·21 + 0·63}{109·4 + 293·2}$

(g) $\dfrac{5·13 \times 18·777}{0·952}$

(h) $\pi \times 9·73^2$

(i) 12% of £2057

12. Decide whether or not the following are reasonable estimates.

Write 'yes' or 'no' for each part.
(a) The total weight of thirty 14 year-olds = 1500 kg.

(b) The time taken by an international athlete to run one mile = 240 s.

(c) The total weight of ten £1 coins = 1 kg.

(d) The top speed of your maths teacher's car = 150 km/h.

(e) The height of a four storey office building = 80 m.

3.3 Interpreting graphs

Travel graphs

- The graph shows the journey of a car from Amble to Cabley via Boldon. The vertical axis shows the distance of the car from Amble between 1400 and 1700.
  (a) At 1530 the car is 60 km from Amble.

  (b) The car stopped at Boldon for 45 minutes.

  (c) The car takes $\frac{1}{2}$ hour to travel 50 km from Amble to Boldon. Thus the speed of the car is 100 km/h.

  (d) The speed of the car from Boldon to Cabley is 40 km/h.

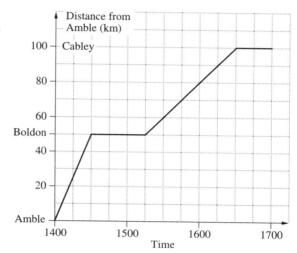

- This graph shows the details of a cycle ride that Jim took starting from his home.
  (a) In the first hour Jim went 30 km so his speed was 30 km/h.

  (b) He stopped for $\frac{1}{2}$ hour at a place 30 km from his home.

  (c) From 0930 until 1100 he cycled back home.

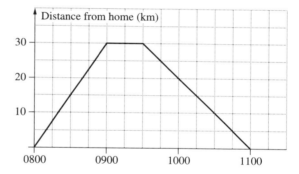

Exercise 1

1. The graph shows a car journey from A to C via B.
   (a) How far is it from A to C?

   (b) For how long does the car stop at B?

   (c) When is the car half way between B and C?

   (d) What is the speed of the car
       (i) between A and B?
       (ii) between B and C?

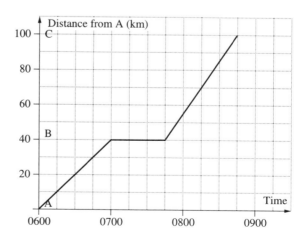

2.

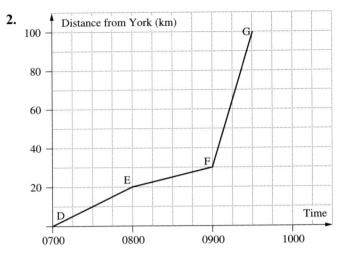

The graph shows the motion of a train as it accelerates away from York.
(a) How far from York is the train at 0730?
(b) When is the train half way between E and F?
(c) Find the speed of the train
    (i) from D to E
    (ii) from F to G

3.

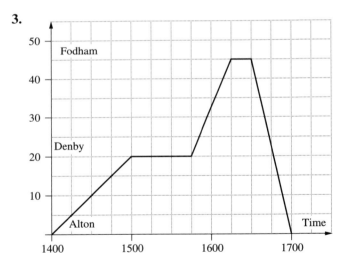

The graph shows a car journey from Alton.
(a) For how long did the car stop at Denby?
(b) When did the car arrive back at Alton?
(c) When did the car leave Denby after stopping?
(d) Find the speed of the car
    (i) from Alton to Denby
    (ii) from Fodham back to Alton

4. The graph shows the journey of a coach and a lorry along the same road between Newcastle and Carlisle.

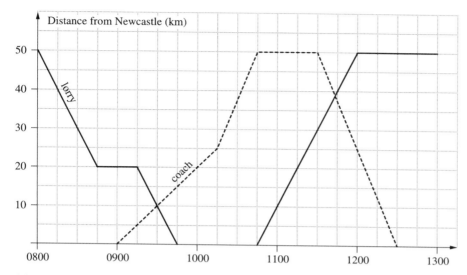

(a) How far apart were the two vehicles at 0915?

(b) At what time did the vehicles meet for the first time?

(c) At what speed did the coach return to Newcastle?

(d) What was the highest speed of the lorry during its journey?

5. The graph shows the motion of three cars A, B and C during a race of length 140 km.

(a) What was the order of the cars after 40 minutes?

(b) Which car won the race?

(c) How far behind A was C after 90 minutes?

(d) After how many minutes did B overtake A?

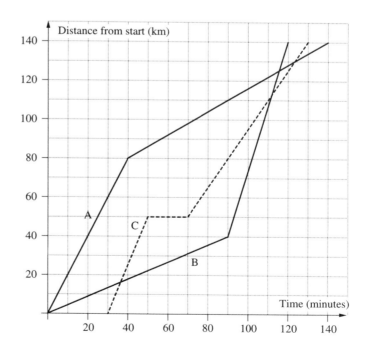

6. The diagram shows the travel graphs of five objects.
Which graph shows:
(a) A car ferry from Dover to Calais
(b) A hovercraft from Dover to Calais
(c) A car ferry from Calais to Dover
(d) A buoy outside Dover harbour
(e) A cross channel swimmer from Dover?

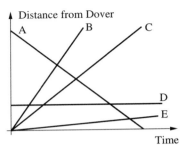

Solving problems with travel graphs

Exercise 2

In Questions **1** to **4** use the same scales as in question 4 of the last exercise.

1. At 13 00 Jo leaves her home and cycles at 10 km/h for 1 hour. She stops for $\frac{1}{2}$ hour and then continues her journey at a speed of 20 km/h for the next 1 hour. She then stops for $\frac{1}{2}$ hour. Finally she returns home at a speed of 30 km/h.

Draw a travel graph to show Jo's journey.
When did she arrive home?

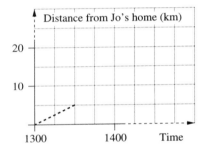

2. Suzy leaves home at 13 00 on her horse and rides at a speed of 20 km/h for one hour.
Suzy and her horse then rest for 45 minutes and afterwards continue their journey at a speed of 15 km/h for another one hour.
At what time do they finish the journey?

3. As Mrs Sadler leaves home in her car at 13 00 she encounters heavy traffic and travels at only 20 km/h for the first $\frac{1}{2}$ hour. In the second half hour she increases her speed to 30 km/h and after that she travels along the main road at 40 km/h for $\frac{3}{4}$ h. She stops at her destination for $\frac{1}{2}$ hour and then returns home at a steady speed of 40 km/h.

4. At 14 00 Mr Toms leaves home and drives at a speed of 20 km/h. At 14 30 he increases his speed to 40 km/h and continues to his destination which is 50 km from home. He stops for $\frac{1}{2}$ hour and then returns home at a speed of 50 km/h.

Use a graph to find the time at which he arrives home.

Exercise 3

1. The step graph shows the cost of travelling on a bus. [Note that an open dot, o, means the overlap point is not included.]
Find the cost of travelling
   (a) 7 miles
   (b) 22 miles
   (c) 10 miles

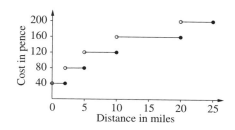

2. The graph below shows the depth of water at the centre of a puddle one summer day.

   Describe what might be happening at each stage A–B, B–C, etc.

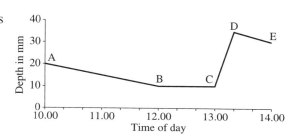

3. The graph shows the water level in a bath. Use the letters A, B, C etc to describe when the events below occurred. [For example: A → B '.....................']

   • John got out of bath
   • Water drained from bath
   • John got into bath
   • Both taps on
   • Hot tap on alone
   • More hot water added when John was in bath
   • John lies in bath, solving equations in his head.

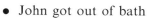

4. Which of the graphs A to D below best fits the following statement:
'The price of paint is still rising, but by less each month.'

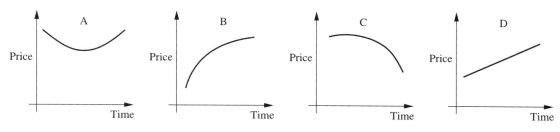

5. Which of the graphs A to D below best fits each of the following statements:
   (a) The examination pass rate, which has been rising steadily, is now beginning to fall.
   (b) The price of computers has fallen steadily over the last year.
   (c) The birthrate was falling but is now steady.
   (d) The cost of holidays, which rose slowly until 1998, is now rising fast.

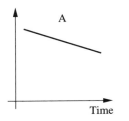
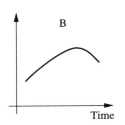
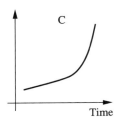
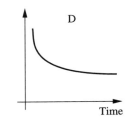

6. Water is poured at a constant rate into each of the containers A, B and C.
The graphs X, Y and Z shows how the water level rises.
Decide which graph fits each container.
State your reasons.

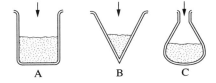

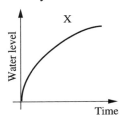
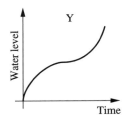
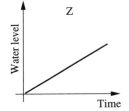

7. Water is poured at a constant rate into three different containers P, Q and R. Draw sketch graphs, similar to those above, to show how the water level would rise in each one.

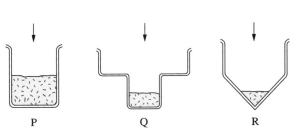

8.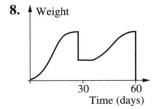
The line graph shows how the weight of an earthworm varies over the first 60 days of its life. Describe the main features of the graph and speculate about the possible causes of the main events.

3.4 Volume

Cuboids

To find the volume of a cuboid, you
multiply the length by the width
by the height.

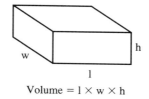

Volume = l × w × h

The volume of a cuboid measuring 2 cm by 3 cm by 5 cm is 30 cm³.
(pronounced '30 centimetres cubed')

Prisms

The volume of the object shown can
be found by dividing the object into
layers, indicated by the thick lines.
Each layer contains 6 cubes and there
are 4 layers. The volume of the object
is 24 cm³.

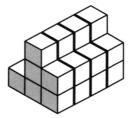

An object which can be cut into identical layers like this is called a
prism.
A prism has the same cross section throughout its length.

Volume of a prism = (Area of cross section) × (length)

Any cuboid is a prism since it has the same cross section throughout
its length.

Find the volume of the prism shown.
All the angles are right angles and
the dimensions are in cm.

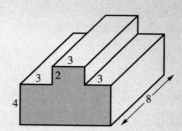

Area of cross section = 4 × (3 + 3 + 3) + (3 × 2)
$\qquad$ = 42 cm².
Volume of prism = 42 × 8
$\qquad$ = 336 cm³

Units

The volume of a liquid is usually given in litres or millilitres (ml)

1000 ml = 1 litre

and 1 ml is the same as $1\,cm^3$.

The diagram shows a cubic metre of water.

$$1\,m^3 = 100 \times 100 \times 100\,cm^3$$
$$= 1\,000\,000\,cm^3$$

So $1\,m^3 = 1\,000\,000\,ml$
$$= 1000\,litres$$

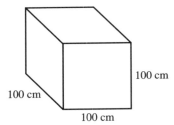

Exercise 1

Find the volume of each prism.

1. Area of end = 3 cm²

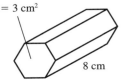

8 cm

2. Area of end = 7 m²

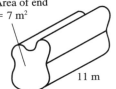

11 m

3.

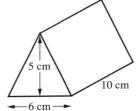

5 cm

6 cm

10 cm

4.

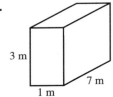

5 cm

4 cm

2 cm

5.

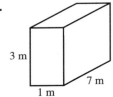

3 m

1 m

7 m

6.

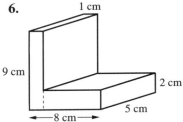

1 cm

9 cm

8 cm

5 cm

2 cm

In Questions **7** to **9** find the volume of each prism. All the angles are right angles and the dimensions are in centimetres.

7.

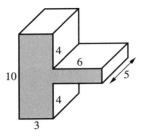

10

4

6

5

4

3

8.

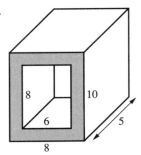

8

10

6

5

8

9.

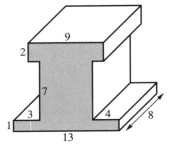

9

2

7

3

4

8

1

13

Exercise 2

1. Which of the solids below are prisms?

(a) 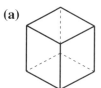   **(b)**    **(c)** 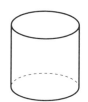   **(d)**    **(e)**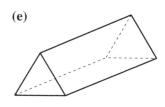

(f)   **(g)** 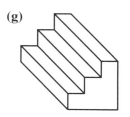   **(h)** 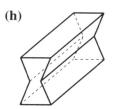   **(i)**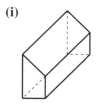

2. A long jump pit is 2·4 m wide by 18 m long and 20 cm deep. What volume of sand is required to fill it? [Hint: Be careful with the units. Change 20 cm into metres and give the answer in m^3.]

3. A box of cornflakes has dimensions 24 cm by 16 cm by 6 cm. How many will fit into a packing case which measures 24 cm by 64 cm by 30 cm?

 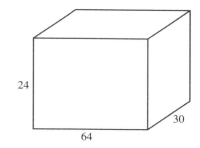

4. How many boxes of matches 10 cm by 2 cm by 6 cm will fit into a packing case 1 m by 80 cm by 48 cm?

5. Find the volume, in litres, of the water trough shown.

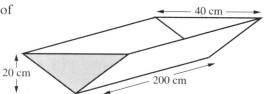

6. Find the capacity, in litres, of a rectangular tank with internal dimensions 60 cm by 20 cm by 1 m. [1 litre = 1000 cm^3]

7. Some steps are to be made in concrete.
Calculate, in cubic metres, the volume of concrete needed.

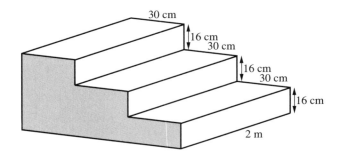

8. Calculate the surface area of each cuboid.

(a)

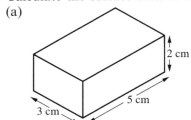

(b)

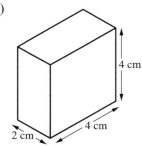

(c)

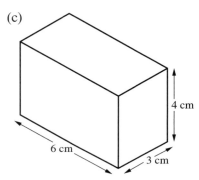

9. The total surface area of a cube is $150\,cm^2$. What is its volume?

10. A uniform metal rod of length $5\,m$ has a volume of $3750\,cm^3$.
Find the area of the cross-section of the rod.

11. The diagram shows the cross section of a swimming pool.
Water is pumped into the pool at a rate of 20 litres/sec.
How long, in hours and minutes, will it take to fill the pool?

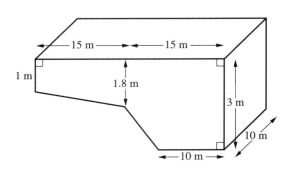

12. Copy and complete,

(a) $1\,m^3 = \boxed{}\,cm^3$

(b) 1 litre $= \boxed{}\,cm^3$

(c) $1\,cm^3 = \boxed{}\,mm^3$

(d) $1\,m^2 = \boxed{}\,cm^2$

(e) $1\,cm^2 = \boxed{}\,mm^2$

(f) $1000\,cm^2 = \boxed{}\,m^2$

Cylinders

A cylinder is a prism because it
has the same cross section throughout
its length.

Volume = (area of cross section) × (length)

$$\text{Volume} = \pi r^2 h$$

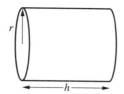

(a) A cylinder has radius 3 cm and
length 10 cm.
Find the volume of the cylinder.

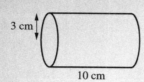

$V = \pi r^2 h$
$V = \pi \times 3^2 \times 10$
$V = 283 \text{ cm}^3$

(b) Find the capacity, in litres, of the oil
drum shown

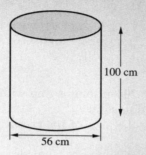

The oil drum is a cylinder.
Volume of oil drum $= \pi \times 28^2 \times 100$
$= 246\,000 \text{ cm}^3$
Capacity of oil drum = 246 litres

Exercise 3

Give answers correct to 1 decimal place where necessary.

1. Find the volume of each cylinder.

(a)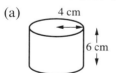

(b)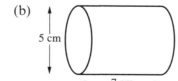

(c)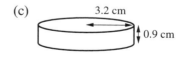

(d)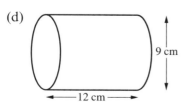

(e)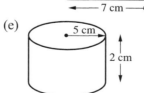

(f)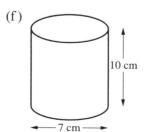

2. Cylinders are cut along the axis of symmetry. Find the volume of each object.

(a)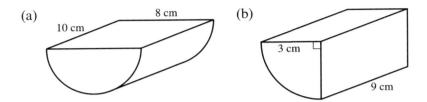

(b)

3. Find the volume in litres of a cylindrical tank of radius 40 cm and height 35 cm.

4. The lead in an unsharpened pencil is in the shape of a cylinder of diameter 2 mm and length 16 cm. Find the volume of the lead in cm^3.

5. A mine shaft 200 m long is dug with the cross-section shown.
 (a) Calculate the area of the cross-section.
 (b) Calculate the volume of earth which must be removed to make way for the shaft.

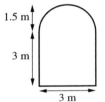

6. Water is poured from the full cylinder A into the empty tank B. Will all the water go in?

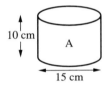

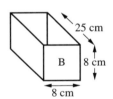

7. An empty cylindrical tank of height 70 cm and diameter 100 cm is to be filled from a tap which delivers water at the rate of 150 ml per second. How long will it take to fill the tank? Give your answer to the nearest minute.

8. How many times can the cylindrical glass be filled from the large drum which is full of milk?

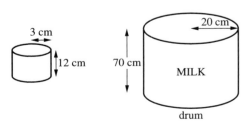

3.5 Charts and graphs

Frequency charts

In the past you have learned how to draw bar charts to represent information (or *data*). In this section you will concentrate on interpreting graphs. The questions are designed to test your understanding of different situations.

Exercise 1

1. A nurse records the ages of all the children who visit her clinic as shown in the table. Make a tally chart to show how many children of each age were seen during the whole week.

	Ages of children in clinic									
M	2	3	1	4	7	9				
Tu	5	5	7	2	4	6				
W	6	6	3	2	4					
Th	1	1	1	1	2	1	1	1	1	1
F	4	7	8	1	3	5	4			

(a) What was the most common age of the children?
(b) The nurse thought that most of the children were aged 2 or under. Was she correct?
(c) One day of the week was reserved for a routine check-up for children of a certain age. What day do you think that was? Give a reason.

2. At a medical inspection the 11/12 year-olds in a school have their heights measured. The results are shown.

147	159	155	144	152	144	151
137	146	141	147	151	145	155
150	138	147	157	143	146	147

(a) Put the heights into groups

class interval	frequency
$135 \leqslant h < 140$	
$140 \leqslant h < 145$	
$145 \leqslant h < 150$	

(b) Draw a frequency diagram

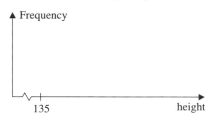

[The group '$135 \leqslant h < 140$' means heights greater than or equal to 135 cm and less than 140 cm]

3. The heights of the children in a holiday camp are shown. Which of the statements below gives the best description of the children?

  A: 'Most of the children were about the same height'
  B: 'Most of the children were either tall or short.'
  C: 'There were far more tall children than short children.'

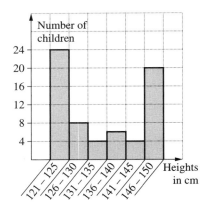

4. A class was split into two groups A and B and both groups were given the same spelling test.

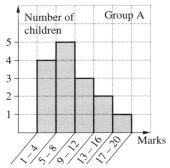

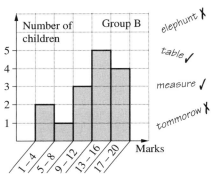

  (a) How many children in group B got a mark of 13 or more?
  (b) One group were allowed to learn the words on the day before the test. Which group do you think that was?
  (c) Say why you chose that group in part (b).

5. The pupils, parents and teachers at a school baked lots of cakes for a charity cake sale. Altogether 200 people baked at least one cake.

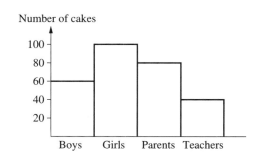

  (a) Alice said 'More girls than boys baked cakes for the sale.' Decide if this statement is: 'True', 'False' or 'Cannot tell'.
  (b) Explain your answer.
  (c) Use the graph to work out the mean number of cakes baked by each of the 200 people who took part.

6. A farmer grows carrots in two different fields. In one field he uses a new fertilizer and in the other he uses the old fertilizer. The diagrams show the weight of the carrots he dug up from each field.

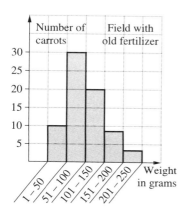

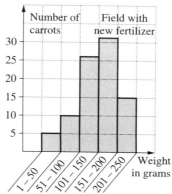

In one sentence describe what effect the new fertilizer had.

7. The graph shows the number of books read in one month by the pupils in a class.

(a) How many pupils were in the class?

(b) Can you use the graph to tell you *exactly* how many books were read?

(c) Explain your answer.

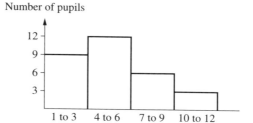

8. The sport of mud wrestling is best played when the ground is made soft by plenty of rainfall. The World Mudwrestling Association (W.M.A.) have to choose a venue for the 2003 championships. They have past rainfall data for the relevant month for two potential towns, Ortega and Pantena. Which venue would be more suitable? Explain your answer.

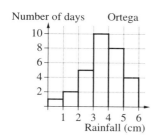

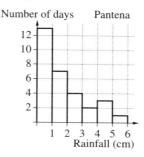

9. The charts show annual temperature and rainfall for two cities.
Write one sentence about each chart to describe the main features.

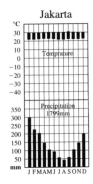

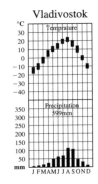

10.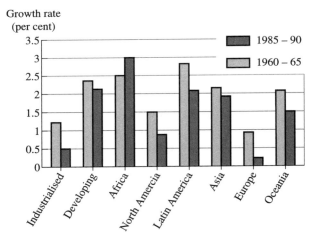

Here are population pyramids for Turkey and Australia. The charts show, for example, that about 4% of the male population of Australia is aged 0–4.

What are the main differences in the two charts? Try to explain why this might be so.

11. The chart shows population growth rates in various parts of the world.

(a) What was the growth rate in North America between 1960 and 1965?

(b) Which region has seen an increase in growth rate?

(c) Which areas currently have the highest and lowest growth rates? Try to think of reasons to explain the differences.

[SOURCE: United Nations Populations Division, World Population Prospects 1990, New York, 1991]

Pie charts

Exercise 2

1. The pie chart shows the results of a survey in which 200 people were asked what they thought was the most important modern invention.
   Copy this table and fill it in.

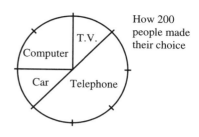

How 200 people made their choice

Choice	computer	T.V.	telephone	car
Number of people				

2. Lara had £24 to spend on presents.
   The pie chart shows how much she spent on each person.
   How much did she spend on:
   (a) her mum   (b) her dad
   (c) her brother   (d) her auntie
   (e) her friend   (f) her grandma?

   [Make sure that your answers add up to £24.]

3. This pie chart shows the afterschool activities of 200 pupils.
   (a) How many pupils do drama? [Hint: work out $360° \div 36°$]
   (b) How many pupils do sport?
   (c) How many pupils do computing?

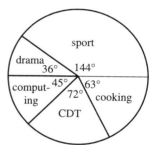

4. Opinion pollsters asked over a thousand people which TV channel they like best. Their answers were:

   ITV   30%
   Channel 4   15%
   Satellite   20%
   BBC1   27%
   BBC2   8%

   Find the angle on a pie chart representing
   (a) Channel 4   (b) BBC1.

5. A packet of breakfast cereal weighing 480 g contains four ingredients:

   Oats   120 g
   Barley   80 g
   Wheat   60 g
   Rye   220 g

   Calculate the angles on a pie chart.

6. The children at a school were asked to state their favourite sport. Here are the results.

Boys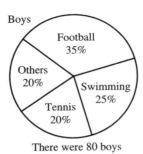
Girls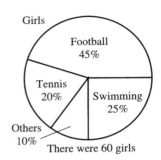

James says 'The same number of boys and girls chose tennis'.
Mel says 'More boys than girls chose swimming'.
(a) Use both charts to explain whether or not James is right.
(b) Use both charts to explain whether or not Mel is right.

7. The pie charts show how much money two shopkeepers get from selling different products.

Mr. Brown

Mrs. Evans

(a) Mr Brown gets £180 from selling ice cream. Estimate how much he get from selling sweets.
(b) From all sales: Mr Brown gets a total of £800 and
            Mrs Evans gets a total of £1200.
Estimate how much each shopkeeper gets from selling magazines.

8. The people in a town were asked to state which supermarket they shopped at most often. The table and the pie chart show the results.

Asda   10%
Tesco   45%
Somerfield   5%
Safeway   ?
Sainsbury   ?

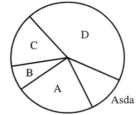

(a) Which sector, either A, B, C or D is for
    (i) Somerfield   (ii) Tesco?
(b) In the survey more people said Sainsbury than Safeway.
    Which sector is for Sainsbury?
    Which sector is for Safeway?
(c) Estimate the percentage who said
    (i) Sainsbury   (ii) Safeway
[Make sure your percentages add up to 100.]

3.6 Mid-book review

Exercise 1

1. Write in index form
  (a) $7 \times 7 \times 7 \times 7 \times 7$ (b) $3 \times 3 \times 3 \times 3 \times 3 \times 3 \times 3 \times 3 \times 3$

2. Simplify the following:
  (a) $4^3 \times 4^2$ (b) $5^7 \times 5^2$ (c) $10^7 \div 10^3$

3. Work out without a calculator.
  (a) $2555 \div 7$ (b) $4807 - 3754$ (c) $2 \cdot 1 \times 0 \cdot 7$
  (d) $4 \cdot 96 \div 0 \cdot 2$ (e) 45×32 (f) $0 \cdot 4 \div 0 \cdot 05$

4.

> ### Bargain brides
> *From Mr Cecil Irwin*
>
> Sir, I am aware that the climate is changing, but not as fast as might be suggested by the following offer seen at Woolworth's of Valentine cards inscribed "To my wife for ever"– three for the price of two.

The Valentine cards normally cost 99p. How much did Mr Irwin pay for three cards?

5. Solve the equations.
  (a) $3x - 1 = 26$ (b) $4x - 1 = 2x + 11$ (c) $3(x - 2) = 9$

6. The diagram shows a rectangle. Work out x and then find the area of the rectangle.

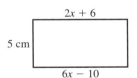

7. Find the missing digits
  (a) $\square\square\square \div 4 = 44$ (b) $\square\square \times 7 = 364$
  (c) $\square\square - 29 = 69$ (d) $\square\square\square \div 8 = 53$

8. Find the area of each shape. Give your answers correct to 1 d.p.
  (a)   (b)   (c)

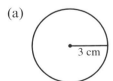 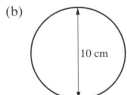 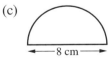

9. Work out:
  (a) $\frac{3}{5} \times \frac{5}{8}$ (b) $\frac{3}{8} \div \frac{1}{4}$ (c) $\frac{3}{4} - \frac{1}{16}$

10. Here are three scatter graphs. Describe briefly what each graph shows.

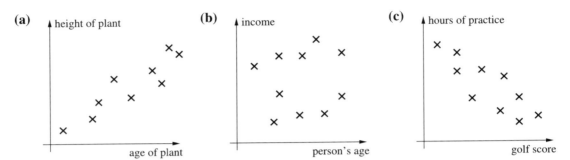

(a) height of plant / age of plant

(b) income / person's age

(c) hours of practice / golf score

Exercise 2

1. Each face of a pyramid is an isosceles triangle with base 30 m and vertical height 22 m. Calculate the area of each face.

2. If we require an estimate of 82×43, to the nearest thousand, we may write $82 \times 43 \approx 80 \times 40$ [$\approx$ means 'equals approximately']
$$= 3200$$
$$= 3000 \text{ to the nearest thousand.}$$

Use this method to estimate the value of the following.
(a) 71×69 (b) 998×41 (c) 11×607 (d) 497×206

3. The diagram shows an empty swimming pool.
Water is pumped into the pool at a rate of $3 \, \text{m}^3$ per minute. How long will it take to fill the pool?

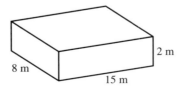

8 m   2 m   15 m

4. The pie charts give data about employment.

(a) What percentage of males are self-employed?

(b) What percentage of females are in full-time education?

(c) What percentage of males are full-time employees?

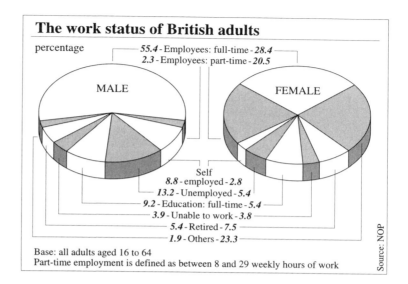

The work status of British adults

percentage — 55.4 - Employees: full-time - 28.4 —
2.3 - Employees: part-time - 20.5

MALE   FEMALE

Self
8.8 - employed - 2.8
13.2 - Unemployed - 5.4
9.2 - Education: full-time - 5.4
3.9 - Unable to work - 3.8
5.4 - Retired - 7.5
1.9 - Others - 23.3

Base: all adults aged 16 to 64
Part-time employment is defined as between 8 and 29 weekly hours of work

Source: NOP

5. The interior angles of a regular polygon are each 135°.
(a) What are the exterior angles?
(b) How many sides has the polygon?

6. Answer true or false:

(a) $3(n-2) = 3n - 2$

(b) $6a \times 3 = 18a$

(c) $n \times n \times n = 3n$

(d) $a + 2b + 3a = 5ab$

(e) $n(n+1) = n^2 + n$

(f) $\dfrac{x}{5} = x \div 5$

Exercise 3

Show all necessary working

1. *Car Hire*

| £13 per day plus |
| 14p per km |

Mr. Hasam hired a car for 6 days and travelled 550 km. How much did it cost?

A £177
B £155
C £77·13
D £771·30

2. A pile of 250 cards is 1 m deep. How thick is each card?

A 0·4 cm
B 0·4 m
C 2·5 cm
D 0·25 cm

3. A ship sails south-west. On what bearing does it sail?

A 045°
B 225°
C 135°
D 315°

4. Which of the statements is(are) true?

1. $a = b$
2. $c = a$
3. $c = d$

A 1 only
B 1 and 2
C 1 and 3
D 1, 2 and 3

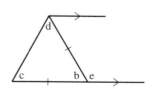

110

Use the graph below for Questions **5** to **8**.

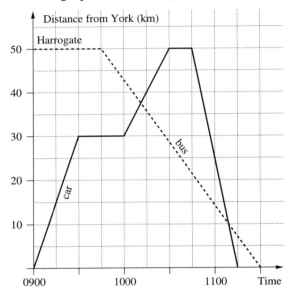

5. When does the car arrive in Harrogate?
- A 0900
- B 0930
- C 1030
- D 1115

6. When does the bus leave Harrogate?
- A 0900
- B 0945
- C 1000
- D 1126

7. At what speed does the car travel on the return journey to York?
- A 30 km/h
- B 40 km/h
- C 50 km/h
- D 100 km/h

8. How far apart are the car and the bus at 1015?
- A 2·5 km
- B 5 km
- C 10 km
- D 22·5 km

9. A piece of wire 48 cm long is bent to form a rectangle in which the length is twice the width. Find the area of the rectangle.
- A 48 cm²
- B 128 cm²
- C 256 cm²
- D 512 cm²

10. Simplify
$$\frac{a+a+a+a+a}{a}$$
- A 4a
- B a⁴
- C 5
- D can't be done

11. The maximum number of obtuse angles in a quadrilateral is
- A 0
- B 1
- C 2
- D 3

12. Which is the largest number?
- A $\frac{1}{5}$
- B 0·2 × 0·4
- C 22%
- D $\frac{21}{100}$

13. Which point does not lie on the line $y = -x$?
- A (−3, −3)
- B (2, −2)
- C (0, 0)
- D (−4, 4)

14. Two dice are rolled and the scores are added to give a total. How many different totals can you get?
- A 6
- B 11
- C 12
- D 36

15. How many wine glasses of capacity 30 ml can be filled from a barrel containing 240 litres?
- A 3
- B 125
- C 800
- D 8000

Exercise 4

Show all necessary working.

1. How many lines of symmetry does the rectangle below have?
- A 1
- B 2
- C 3
- D 4

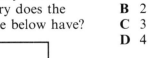

2. A car travels half a mile in a minute. How far does the car travel in one hour?
- A $\frac{1}{2}$ mile
- B 30 miles
- C 60 miles
- D 120 miles

3. The pie chart shows the nationalities of people on a ferry. What angle should be drawn for the UK sector?

    A 10·28°
    B 35°
    C 126°
    D 132°

4. 1 kg = 2·2 pounds. Which is closest to 7 pounds?

    A 3 kg
    B 4 kg
    C 14 kg
    D 15 kg

5. At what point will the line $y = x$ cut the line $x = -3$?

    A $(-3, -3)$
    B $(3, 3)$
    C $(-3, 0)$
    D Impossible to say

6. The value of $1^1 \times 2^2 \times 3^3$ is

    A 6
    B 36
    C 108
    D 216

7. 55% of £55 is

    A £1
    B £55
    C £30·25
    D £28·50

8. Solve the equation $2x - 1 = 11$

    A 6
    B $\frac{1}{6}$
    C 5
    D $\frac{1}{5}$

9. The area of one face of a cube is 9 cm². The total length, in cm, of all the edges of the cube is

    A 36
    B 48
    C 54
    D none of the above

10. How many of the statements below are true?

$$\tfrac{1}{3} > \tfrac{1}{4}, \quad \tfrac{1}{2} + \tfrac{1}{3} = \tfrac{2}{5},$$
$$\tfrac{1}{3} \div \tfrac{1}{4} = 1\tfrac{1}{3}, \quad \tfrac{2}{3} \text{ of } \tfrac{1}{5} = \tfrac{2}{15}$$

    A 1
    B 2
    C 3
    D 4

11. When £306 is divided between three people in the ratio 2:3:4, the largest share is

    A £136
    B £102
    C £34
    D £68

12. Find which of the five numbers below is the mean of the other four. 23, 17, 22, 24, 34

    A 17
    B 22
    C 23
    D 24

13. A length of one inch is approximately

    A 1 cm
    B 2·5 cm
    C 4 cm
    D 30 cm

14. Find the ratio (shaded area) : (unshaded area)

    A 3:4
    B 4:1
    C 3:1
    D $3\tfrac{1}{2} : 1\tfrac{1}{2}$

15. A lottery prize of 4000 million pounds is shared equally between 13 thousand people. About how much does each person receive?

    A £3 million
    B £300 000
    C £30 000
    D £0·3

16. Find the area of the parallelogram in square units.

    A 3
    B $4\tfrac{1}{2}$
    C 6
    D 9

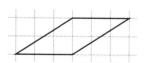

Part 4

4.1 Transformations

Translation

In a translation an object 'shifts' from one position to another. There is no turning or reflection and the object stays the same size. A translation is described completely by its *vector*.

In the diagram:

(a) △A is mapped onto △B by the translation with vector $\begin{pmatrix} 3 \\ 2 \end{pmatrix}$.

(b) △A is mapped onto △C by the translation with vector $\begin{pmatrix} 5 \\ -2 \end{pmatrix}$.

(c) △C is mapped onto △B by the translation with vector $\begin{pmatrix} -2 \\ 4 \end{pmatrix}$.

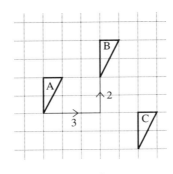

When performing a translation, concentrate your attention on *one* vertex of the shape.

The top number of a vector gives the number of units across (positive to the right). The bottom number gives the number of units up or down (positive upwards).

So $\begin{pmatrix} 5 \\ 2 \end{pmatrix}$ is $\begin{array}{l} \text{5 right } \rightarrow \\ \text{2 up } \uparrow \end{array}$, $\begin{pmatrix} 3 \\ -1 \end{pmatrix}$ is $\begin{array}{l} \text{3 right } \rightarrow \\ \text{1 down } \downarrow \end{array}$

Exercise 1

1. Look at the diagram shown. Write down the vector for each of the following translations:

   (a) △H → △P   (b) △E → △A
   (c) △R → △S   (d) △W → △C
   (e) △Y → △L   (f) △U → △F
   (g) △T → △A   (h) △W → △G
   (i) △O → △Y   (j) △U → △I

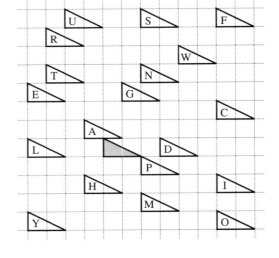

Single transformations

So far in Book 8i and Book 9i you have studied four basic transformations. A full description of each transformation requires the information below.

- To describe a *reflection* you need the equation of the mirror line.

- To describe a *rotation* you need the angle, the direction and the centre of the rotation.

- To describe an *enlargement* you need the scale factor and the centre of the enlargement.

- To describe a *translation* you need the vector.

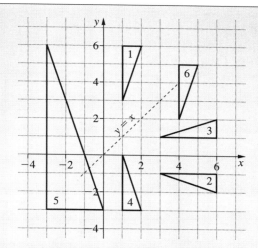

In the diagram the transformations are as follows:

$\triangle 1 \rightarrow \triangle 2$:   Rotation 90° clockwise, centre (0, 0)

$\triangle 1 \rightarrow \triangle 3$:   Reflection in $y = x$

$\triangle 1 \rightarrow \triangle 6$:   Translation $\begin{pmatrix} 3 \\ -1 \end{pmatrix}$

$\triangle 4 \rightarrow \triangle 5$:   Enlargement, scale factor 3, centre (3, −3)

$\triangle 1 \rightarrow \triangle 4$:   Reflection in $y = 1\frac{1}{2}$

$\triangle 2 \rightarrow \triangle 6$:   Rotation 90° anti-clockwise, centre (2, 1)

- Notice that translations, rotations and reflections preserve length and angle and map onto congruent images.

- Enlargements preserve angle but not length.

114

Exercise 2

1. Draw each shape on a squared paper and then draw its reflection.

(a)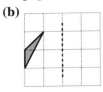

(b)

(c)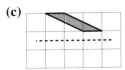

(d)

(e)

(f)

(g)

2. Write down the equation of the mirror line for each reflection.

(a) $\triangle A \rightarrow \triangle B$

(b) $\triangle A \rightarrow \triangle F$

(c) $\triangle E \rightarrow \triangle D$

(d) $\triangle B \rightarrow \triangle C$

(e) $\triangle E \rightarrow \triangle F$

(f) $\triangle F \rightarrow \triangle G$

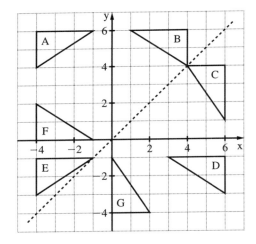

3. Draw each shape and its image under the rotation given.
   Take O as the centre of rotation in each case.

(a)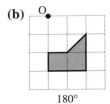

90° anticlockwise

(b)

180°

(c)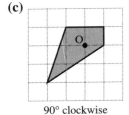

90° clockwise

(d)

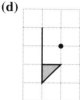

90° clockwise

(e)

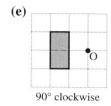

90° clockwise

(f)

90° anticlockwise

4. Describe fully the rotations. (give the angle, direction and centre)

(a) $\Delta A \rightarrow \Delta B$

(b) $\Delta A \rightarrow \Delta C$

(c) $\Delta A \rightarrow \Delta D$

(d) $\Delta E \rightarrow \Delta D$

(e) $\Delta C \rightarrow \Delta E$

(f) $\Delta D \rightarrow \Delta F$

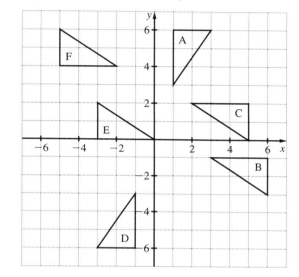

5. Copy each shape with its centre of enlargement. Then enlarge the shape by the scale factor given.

(a)

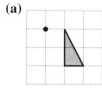

scale factor 2

(b)

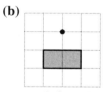

scale factor 2

(c)

scale factor 3

(d)

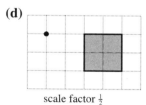

scale factor $\frac{1}{2}$

(e)

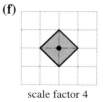

scale factor 3

(f)

scale factor 4

(g)

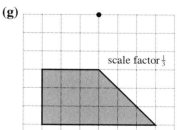

scale factor $\frac{1}{3}$

6. Describe fully each of the following enlargements

(a) $\triangle D \rightarrow \triangle C$

(b) $\triangle A \rightarrow \triangle B$

(c) $\triangle F \rightarrow \triangle E$

(d) $\triangle D \rightarrow \triangle E$

(e) $\triangle B \rightarrow \triangle D$

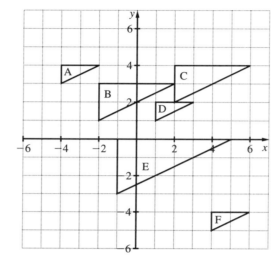

7. Copy the diagram so that you can draw construction lines.

Describe fully each of the following transformations:

(a) $\triangle 1 \rightarrow \triangle 2$

(b) $\triangle 2 \rightarrow \triangle 3$

(c) $\triangle 3 \rightarrow \triangle 4$

(d) $\triangle 1 \rightarrow \triangle 5$

(e) $\triangle 4 \rightarrow \triangle 6$

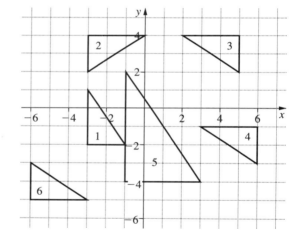

8. (a) Draw axes with x and y from -6 to $+6$.

(b) Plot and label $\triangle 1$ with vertices at $(-6, -2)$, $(-6, -5)$, $(-5, -2)$.

(c) Draw $\triangle 2$, $\triangle 3$, ... $\triangle 7$ as follows:

  (i) $\triangle 1 \rightarrow \triangle 2$ Reflection in $y = x$

  (ii) $\triangle 2 \rightarrow \triangle 3$ Rotation $180°$, centre $(0, -5\frac{1}{2})$

  (iii) $\triangle 3 \rightarrow \triangle 4$ Reflection in $y = -x$

  (iv) $\triangle 3 \rightarrow \triangle 5$ Rotation $90°$ anticlockwise, centre $(0, -3)$

(d) Describe fully each of the following single transformations:

  (i) $\triangle 1 \rightarrow \triangle 4$

  (ii) $\triangle 2 \rightarrow \triangle 5$

Combined transformations

Exercise 3

1. ΔP is reflected in the line $y = x$ to give ΔQ.

   ΔQ is translated with vector $\begin{pmatrix} -1 \\ -5 \end{pmatrix}$ to give ΔR.

   (a) Show that ΔP can also be transformed onto ΔR by a reflection in the x axis followed by a rotation.

   (b) Describe one other way of transforming ΔP onto ΔR. Ask a friend to check your answer.

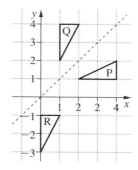

2.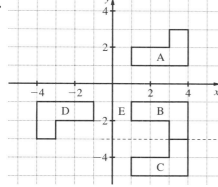

   We have:
   A → B reflection in x axis,
   B → C reflection in $y = -3$,
   B → D reflection in y axis.

   Describe the single transformation:
   (a) A → C
   (b) A → D

3. Find a combination of transformations to map:
   (a) ΔA onto ΔC
   (b) ΔA onto ΔB
   (c) ΔB onto ΔD

   Ask a friend to check your answers.

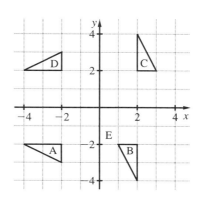

4. (a) Draw axes with x and y from -7 to $+7$.

(b) Plot and label $\triangle 1$ with vertices at $(0, 0)$, $(0, 2)$, $(3, 2)$.

(c) Draw $\triangle 2$, $\triangle 3$, ... $\triangle 7$ as follows:

    (i) $\triangle 1 \rightarrow \triangle 2$ Reflection in $y = 0$ (the x axis)

    (ii) $\triangle 2 \rightarrow \triangle 3$ Reflection in $y = x$

    (iii) $\triangle 1 \rightarrow \triangle 4$ Translation $\begin{pmatrix} -6 \\ 2 \end{pmatrix}$

    (iv) $\triangle 4 \rightarrow \triangle 5$ Translation $\begin{pmatrix} 4 \\ 3 \end{pmatrix}$

    (v) $\triangle 4 \rightarrow \triangle 6$ Reflection in $y = 0$

    (vi) $\triangle 6 \rightarrow \triangle 7$ Reflection in $y = x$

(d) Describe each of the following single transformations:

    (i) $\triangle 1 \rightarrow \triangle 3$

    (ii) $\triangle 1 \rightarrow \triangle 5$

    (iii) $\triangle 1 \rightarrow \triangle 7$

5.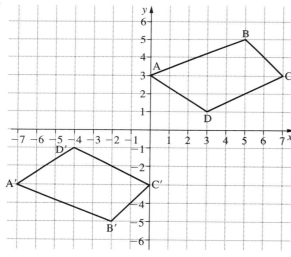

ABCD is mapped onto A′B′C′D′ by a reflection followed by a translation parallel to the x axis.

(a) Describe these two transformations as fully as possible.

(b) Would the image be the same if the translation was completed before the reflection?

6. Draw axes for both x and y between -8 and $+8$.

Plot the points $(1, 1)$, $(3, 1)$, $(3, 2)$, $(2, 2)$, $(2, 4)$ and $(1, 4)$ and join up to make an 'L' shape.

This is mapped onto the points $(-2, -2)$, $(-2, -6)$, $(-4, -6)$, $(-4, -4)$, $(-8, -4)$, $(-8, -2)$ by *two* transformations; an enlargement with centre $(0, 0)$ followed by a reflection. Describe these transformations as fully as possible.

4.2 3D Shapes

Exercise 1

1. 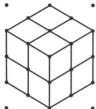 Here is a cube made from eight 1 cm cubes. Draw a cuboid with a volume of $12\,\text{cm}^3$.

Make sure the paper is this way

2. (a) Make this shape using cubes.
   (b) Draw two other isometric views of the shape.

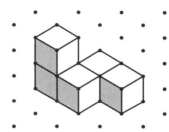

3. 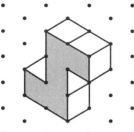 The S-shape falls over onto the shaded face. Draw the shape after it has fallen over.

4. You need 16 cubes. Make the two shapes shown and then arrange them into a $4 \times 4 \times 1$ cuboid by adding a third shape, which you have to find. Draw the third shape on isometric paper. There are *two* possible shapes.

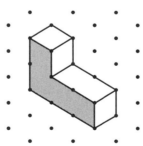 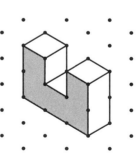

5. (a) Make the S-shape from Question **3** and the two shapes from Question **4**.
   (b) Join the three shapes together and add a fourth shape to make a $4 \times 4 \times 1$ cuboid. Describe the fourth shape.

120

6. Here are two possible nets to make a cube.
For each net decide which face is opposite the shaded face in the cube.

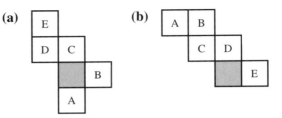

7. The net for a tetrahedron consists of four equilateral triangles.
On isometric paper draw a possible net for a tetrahedron.

8. Draw an accurate net for a square-based pyramid where the vertex is directly above the centre of the base.

9. The diagrams below show four side-views of the model.
Which side-view does each diagram show?

1.   **2.**

3.   **4.**

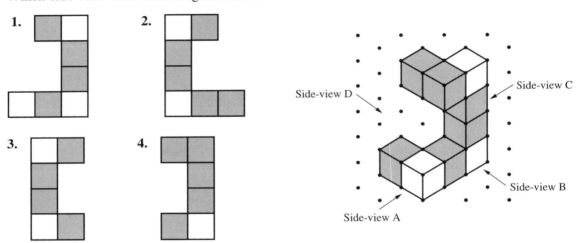

10. The diagram shows a model made with 9 cubes, 5 grey and 4 white.

Draw 5 diagrams to show the side-views A, B, C and D and also the plan view.

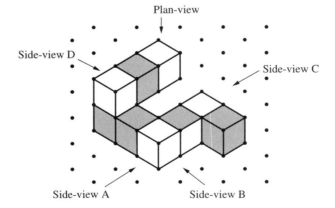

Planes of symmetry

- A plane of symmetry divides a 3-D shape into two congruent shapes. One shape must be a mirror image of the other shape.

The shaded plane is a plane of symmetry of the cube.

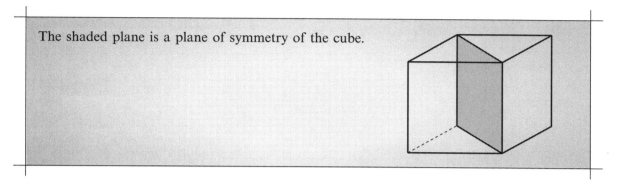

Exercise 2

1. Here is a cuboid and a triangular prism (whose cross-section is an equilateral triangle).

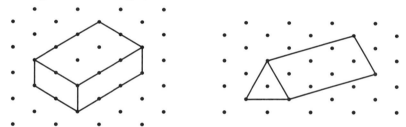

   How many planes of symmetry does each shape have?

2. Here are two shapes made from four cubes. There are eight different shapes which can be made using four cubes.

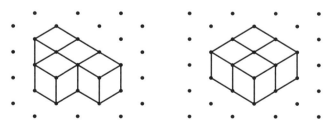

   Make the eight shapes, using cubes, and draw them on isometric paper. Identify any planes of symmetry.

3. Visualise and describe all the planes of symmetry of:
   (a) a square-based pyramid
   (b) a cylinder
   (c) a regular tetrahedron.

4.3 Finding a rule

For the sequence 3, 8, 13, 18, ... the rule is 'add 5'. We draw a mapping diagram with a column for 5 times the term number (i.e. $5n$)

n	$5n$	term
1	5	3
2	10	8
3	15	13
4	20	18

We see that each term is 2 less than $5n$.

So, the 10th term is $(5 \times 10) - 2 = 48$
the 20th term is $(5 \times 20) - 2 = 98$
the nth term is $5 \times n - 2 = 5n - 2$

Exercise 1

1. Look at the sequence 5, 8, 11, 14, ...

The difference between terms is 3.
Copy the table, which has a column for $3n$.
Copy and complete: 'The nth term of the
sequence is $3n + \boxed{}$.'

n	$3n$	term
1	3	5
2	6	8
3	9	11
4	12	14

2. Look at the sequence and the table underneath. Find the nth
term in each case.

(a) Sequence 5, 9, 13, 17, ...

n	$4n$	term
1	4	5
2	8	9
3	12	13
4	16	17

nth term = $\boxed{}$

(b) Sequence 2, 8, 14, 20, ...

n	$6n$	term
1	6	2
2	12	8
3	18	14
4	24	20

nth term = $\boxed{}$

3. In the sequence 6, 11, 16, 21, ...
the difference between terms is 5.
Copy and complete the table and
write an expression for the
nth term of the sequence.

n	$\boxed{}$	term
1	$\boxed{}$	6
2	$\boxed{}$	11
3	$\boxed{}$	16
4	$\boxed{}$	21

4. Look at the sequence 6, 10, 14, 18, ...
Write down the difference between terms.
Make a table like the one in Question **3** and use it to find an expression for the *n*th term.

5. Write down each sequence in a table and then find the *n*th term.
(a) 5, 7, 9, 11, ...
(b) 3, 7, 11, 15, ...
(c) 2, 8, 14, 20, ...

6. Make a table for each sequence and write the *n*th term.
(a) 2, 10, 18, 26, ...
(b) 7, 10, 13, 16, ...
(c) 21, 30, 39, 48, ...

In Questions **7** to **18** you are given a sequence in a table. Copy the table and make an extra column. Find an expression for the *n*th term of each sequence. [*t* stands for 'term']

7.

n	t
1	3
2	8
3	13
4	18
5	23

8.

n	t
1	3
2	6
3	9
4	12
5	15

9.

n	t
1	7
2	13
3	19
4	25
5	31

10.

n	t
1	6
2	8
3	10
4	12
5	14

11.

n	t
1	6
2	7
3	8
4	9
5	10

12.

n	t
1	1
2	4
3	7
4	10
5	13

13.

n	t
1	5
2	13
3	21
4	29
5	37

14.

n	t
1	7
2	12
3	17
4	22
5	27

15.

n	t
6	14
7	17
8	20
9	23
10	26

16.

n	t
8	83
9	93
10	103
11	113
12	123

17.

n	t
4	15
5	18
6	21
7	24

18.

n	t
12	61
13	66
14	71
15	76

124

Exercise 2

1. Here is a sequence of triangles made from a number of matches *m*.

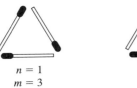 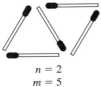 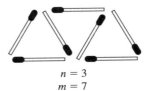

$n = 1$	$n = 2$	$n = 3$
$m = 3$	$m = 5$	$m = 7$

n	m
1	3
2	5
3	7
4	

Draw the next diagram in the sequence and write the values for *n* and *m* in a table. How many matches are in the *n*th term?

In Questions **2** to **5** there are a series of 'matchstick homes'. In each question make a table of values of *n*, the number of homes, and the number of matches. Find an expression for the number of matches in the *n*th term of the sequence.

2. Box homes

  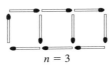

$n = 1$ $n = 2$ $n = 3$

n	matches
1	4
2	
3	

3. Hexagon homes

 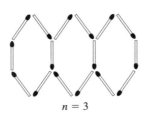

$n = 1$ $n = 2$ $n = 3$

4. Sawtooth homes

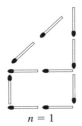 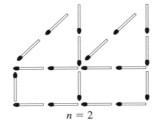 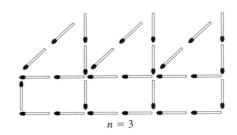

$n = 1$ $n = 2$ $n = 3$

5. Dry car homes

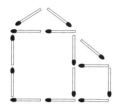 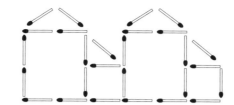

6. Crosses are drawn on rectangular 'dotty' paper. The diagram number of the cross is recorded together with the total number of dots d on each cross.

n	d
1	5
2	9
3	13

How many dots are there in the nth term of the sequence?

7. In each diagram below, a number of white squares w surrounds a rectangle of black squares. The length of each rectangle is one unit more than the height h.

 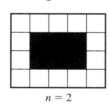 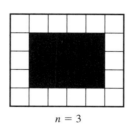

n	w
1	10

Make a table of values of n and w use it to find an expression for the nth term of the sequence

8. Open 'boxes' are drawn on rectangular dotty paper.

Count the number of dots in each diagram and find an expression for the number of dots in the nth term of the sequence.

Substituting into formulas

- In the *formula* $s = ut$, s, u and t are variable quantities, related by the formula.

- A mobile phone company might use a formula like '£18 per month plus 20 pence per minute of call time'

Let B = Phone Bill and
m = call time in minutes.
The formula is $B = 18 + 0{\cdot}2m$

(a) If $m = 10$, $B = 18 + 0{\cdot}2 \times 10$
$B = 18 + 2$
$B = 25$

(b) If $m = 35$, $B = 18 + 0{\cdot}2 \times 35$
$B = 18 + 7$
$B = 25$

Exercise 3

1. Employees at 'Save-A-Lot' superstores are paid using the formula $W = 3{\cdot}5h$, where W = Wage in £ and h = hours worked.
   (a) Find the wage for Bill who worked 8 hours.
   (b) Find the wage for Sue who worked 40 hours.

2. Gary's Garage charges £30 call out charge plus an hourly rate of £25 per hour to attend roadside car breakdowns.
   The formula linking C (cost) and h (hours worked) is
   $C = 25h + 30$.
   (a) Find C if $h = 2$
   (b) Find C if $h = 10$

3. Serge has a mobile phone which costs him £15 per month plus 20p per minute of call time.
   Find his total bill for a month when he has 30 minutes of call time.

4. Ayesha has a mobile phone contract with a different company.
The formula linking B (phone bill) and C (call time in minutes)
is $B = 28 + 0{\cdot}05C$.
(a) Find B, when $C = 100$

(b) Find B, when $C = 10$

5. Here is a formula $c = 7t - 3$.
Find the value of c when

(a) $t = 2$ (b) $t = 10$ (c) $t = \frac{1}{2}$

6. Using the formula $p = 70 - 4x$, find the value of p when

(a) $x = 1$ (b) $x = 10$ (c) $x = 20$

7. The charge, £C, made by a chef to cook for a group of p people
is given by the formula

$C = 7p + 65.$

(a) What is the charge for a group of 20 people?
(b) How many people are in the group if the charge is £282?

8. Here are two formulas involving the sides of a square:
      Perimeter, $P = 4L$
      Area, $A = L^2$

(a) Find P, if $L = 15$
(b) Find A, if $L = 9$
(c) Find L, if $P = 80$
(d) Find L, if $A = 100$

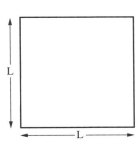

9. The perimeter of a rectangle (P) is linked to the length of its
base (b) and height (h) by the formula $P = 2b + 2h$.
(a) Find P, if $b = 5$ and $h = 3$.

(b) Find P, if $b = 8$ and $h = 1$

(c) Find b, if $P = 30$ and $h = 5$

10. Below are several different formulae for z in terms of x.
Find the value of z in each case.
(a) $z = 15x - 60$, $x = 4$

(b) $z = 2(3x + 5)$, $x = -1$

(c) $z = \dfrac{10 - x}{2}$, $x = 5$

Exercise 4

1. The formula for the area of a
   triangle is $A = \frac{1}{2}BH$
   (a) Find A, if $B = 10$ and $H = 6$
   (b) Find B, if $A = 20$ and $H = 4$

2. In the formulae below t is given in terms of n and a.
   Find the value of t in each case.
   (a) $t = 3a - 10n$; $a = 5$, $n = 1$
   (b) $t = 20a + 7n - 4$; $a = 1$, $n = 2$
   (c) $t = an + 11$; $a = 4$, $n = 3$
   (d) $t = 5(3a + 8n)$; $a = 0$, $n = 1$

3. If $T = 3y + 4y^2$, find the values of T when
   (a) $y = 1$ (b) $y = 3$ (c) $y = -1$
   [Remember $4y^2 = 4(y^2)$]

4. If $A = d^2 - 3d + 5$, find the values of A when
   (a) $d = 2$ (b) $d = 5$ (c) $d = 10$

5. The velocity, v, of an
   accelerating snowmobile is
   given by the formula
       $v = u + at$.
   Find v when $u = 0$, $a = 22.5$
   and $t = 3$.

6. An approximate formula linking temperatures in Fahrenheit and
   Celsius is $F = 2C + 30$, where F is temperature in degrees
   Fahrenheit and C is temperature in degrees Celsius.
   (a) Find F, if $C = 8$
   (b) Find C, if $F = 56$

7. The weight w of the brain of a
   Stegosaurus is connected to its
   age, A, and its intelligence
   quotient, I, by the formula

   $$w = \frac{A^2 + I/A}{5000}$$

   Find w, when $A = 20$ and $I = 2$.

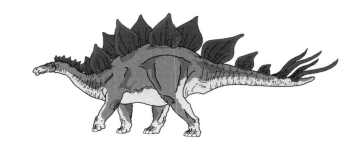

Expressions

An expression does *not* have an equals sign. For example: $3x - 7$; $x^2 + 7y$; $ab - c^2$. These are all expressions.

Below are three expressions involving a, b and c. Find the value of each expression given that $a = 5$
$b = -2$
$c = 3$

(i) $\quad 3a - c$
$= 3 \times 5 - 3$
$= 15 - 3$
$= 12$

(ii) $\quad 2b + a$
$= 2(-2) + 5$
$= -4 + 5$
$= 1$

(iii) $\quad 3c - 4b$
$= 3(3) - 4(-2)$
$= 9 + 8$
$= 17$

Notice that the working goes *down* the page, not across. This helps to avoid errors.

Exercise 5

Find the value of the expressions given that $\quad a = 5$
$b = -2$
$c = 3$
$d = -1$

1. $5a - c$ **2.** $2b + a$ **3.** $a + d$ **4.** $3c + b$

5. $4b + c$ **6.** $2d - a$ **7.** $5b + 10$ **8.** $a + b + c$

9. $b + c$ **10.** $7 - 2a$ **11.** $25 + 5b$ **12.** $3a + 4d$

13. $a^2 + b^2$ **14.** $ac + b$ **15.** $6 - 2c$ **16.** $d^2 + 4$

17. $ab + c$ **18.** $5d - 2c$ **19.** $b^2 + cd$ **20.** $5a + b + d$

21. $bd + c^2$ **22.** $2(a - c)$ **23.** $3(a + d)$ **24.** $a(c + b)$

In Questions **25** to **44** find the value of the expressions given that $m = 2$
$n = 0$
$p = -3$
$q = 4$

25. $mn + q$ **26.** $p + q$ **27.** $2m + p$ **28.** pq

29. $p^2 + n^2$ **30.** $2n - p$ **31.** $mp + n$ **32.** $4(p + q)$

33. $5(m + p)$ **34.** $10 - 2q$ **35.** $m - p$ **36.** $m(m + q)$

37. m^3 **38.** $p + p^2$ **39.** $5m + p + q$ **40.** p^3

41. $q(p + m)$ **42.** $m + m^2 + m^3$ **43.** $3q - 2p$ **44.** $n(m^2 - pq)$

4.4 Percentages

The use of percentages is very important in mathematics but unfortunately they are misunderstood by many people in everyday life.

This section begins with a review of the topics covered in Book 8i.

(a) Work out 18% of £5600

Either: 18% of £5600
$= \frac{18}{100} \times \frac{5600}{1}$
$= £1008$

Or: 18% of £5600
$= 0 \cdot 18 \times 5600$
$= £1008$

(b) Change a mark of 17 out of 40 into a percentage.
∴ Answer $= \frac{17}{40} \times 100$
$= 42 \cdot 5\%$

> To change a fraction to a percentage, multiply by 100

(c) Work out 6·3% of £68·99, correct to the nearest penny.

6·3% of £68·99
$= \frac{6 \cdot 3}{100} \times \frac{68 \cdot 99}{1}$
$= £4 \cdot 34637$
$= £4 \cdot 35$ (to the nearest penny)

Exercise 1

1. Work out.
   (a) 11% of £245
   (b) 18% of £2300
   (c) 74% of £6100
   (d) 7·5% of £350
   (e) 4% of £6·50
   (f) 130% of £85

2. Work out, correct to the nearest penny.
   (a) 3% of £8·24
   (b) 11% of £18·99
   (c) 39% of £59·95
   (d) 18% of £5·90
   (e) 4·6% of £18·99
   (f) 12·5% of £6·95

3. (a) Work out the volume of a standard size box of Corn Flakes.
   (b) What is the volume of a *special offer* box of Corn Flakes which is 40% bigger?
   (c) The standard size box contains enough Corn Flakes to fill 20 cereal bowls. How many bowls can be filled from the 'special offer' box of Corn Flakes?

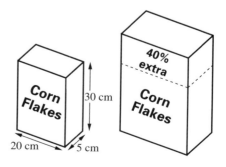

4. Change these fractions to percentages

(a) $\frac{1}{5}$ (b) $\frac{3}{4}$ (c) $\frac{7}{8}$ (d) $\frac{17}{20}$

(e) $\frac{44}{80}$ (f) $\frac{63}{120}$ (g) $\frac{71}{100}$ (h) $\frac{19}{25}$

5. Farmer Jones owns three farms: Hill Farm; Dane Farm; Stone Farm.

(a) Here is a plan of Hill Farm.
About 30% of the land is for cattle.
  (i) *About* what percentage of the land is for sheep?
  (ii) *About* what percentage of the land is for pigs?

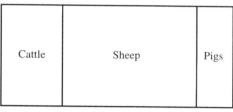

Hill farm

(b) Dane Farm is used for crops, as shown. *About* what fraction of the land is used for potatoes?

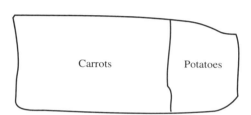

(c) Stone Farm is used for turkeys and ducks. If 38% of the land is used for turkeys, what percentage is used for ducks?

6. In a Physics test, Sima got 52 out of 80. What was her mark as a percentage?

7. What percentage of the letters in the box are
(a) vowels?
(b) the letter R?
Give your answers correct to 1 d.p.

S	M	O	K	I	N	G	I	S
N	O	T	P	A	R	T	I	C
U	L	A	R	L	Y	G	O	O
D	F	O	R	Y	O	U	O	K

8. A breakfast cereal contains the following ingredients by weight:
Toasted Oat Flakes 720 g, Raw Sugar 34 g, Oat Bran 76 g, Honey 26 g, Banana 57 g, Hazelnuts 12 g.
What percentage of the packet is Oat Bran? Give your answer correct to one decimal place.

9. The table shows the results when three makes of car were tested for a particular fault in the ventilation system.
   (a) What percentage of the cars which failed were Fords?
   (b) What percentage of the Rolls Royce cars failed?

	Rolls Royce	Renault	Ford
Failed	2	13	25
Passed	17	474	1756
Total			

10. Copy and complete the table.

	Fraction	Decimal	Percentage
(a)	$\frac{4}{5}$		
(b)		0·125	
(c)			2%
(d)	$\frac{2}{3}$		

Increasing or decreasing by a percentage

Mathematicians always look for quick ways of solving problems. The question in the box below is solved first by an 'ordinary' method and secondly by a 'quick' method. You can choose for yourself which method you prefer.

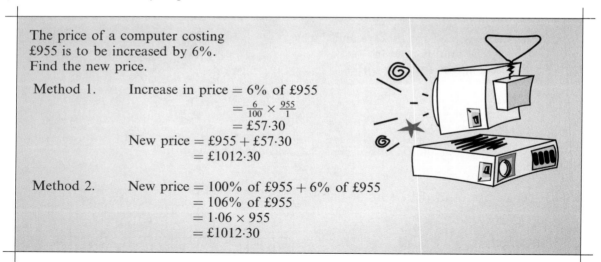

The price of a computer costing £955 is to be increased by 6%. Find the new price.

Method 1.   Increase in price = 6% of £955
$$= \frac{6}{100} \times \frac{955}{1}$$
$$= £57\cdot30$$
New price = £955 + £57·30
$$= £1012\cdot30$$

Method 2.   New price = 100% of £955 + 6% of £955
$$= 106\% \text{ of } £955$$
$$= 1\cdot06 \times 955$$
$$= £1012\cdot30$$

(a) Increase a price of £6800 by 17%

New price = 100% of £6800
+17% of £6800
= 117% of £6800
= 1·17 × 6800
= £7956

(b) Decrease a price of £584 by 2%

New price = 100% of £584
−2% of £584
= 98% of £584
= 0·98 × 584
= £572·32

Exercise 2

1. (a) Increase £120 by 35%
   (b) Increase 80 kg by 40%
   (c) Decrease $400 by 15%
   (d) Decrease 350 km by 60%

2. The 2002 price of a motor bike is £8580. Calculate the 2003 price, which is 5% higher.

3. Find the new price of a necklace costing £85, after the price is reduced by 7%.

4. The 'Hairy Scarebellies' debut C.D. cost £12 when it was first released, but it is so rare that copies have increased 40% in value since then. What are they worth now?

5. A jacket costing £130 is reduced by 25% in the latest sale. Find its sale price.

6. Stan is delighted to find out that his guitar has increased 60% in value. He bought it in 1988 for £450. What is it worth now?

7. Alfonse has found that most new cars are worth only 40% of their original value after 3 years.
   (a) How much will a £13 500 car be worth after 3 years?
   (b) How much, in pounds, has it lost in value?

8. 'Gloddings' stately home was valued at £800 000 when Lord and Lady Campbell first bought it. Since then it has increased by 48% in value. What is it worth now?

9. Rajesh bought 500 shares in 'Ruthless Incorporated' at £2·31 each.

   (a) Find the total value of his shares.
   (b) Find the total value of his shares after a drop of 27% in value.

Percentage change

Suppose the price of a car was
increased from £8000 to £8100 and the
price of a pair of speakers was
increased from £200 to £300. The
actual increase of £100 is the same for
both items but the increase is far more
significant for the speakers!
A good way of comparing price
changes (up or down) is to work out
the *percentage* change.

For an increase use the formula,

$$\text{percentage increase} = \left(\frac{\text{actual increase}}{\text{original value}}\right) \times 100$$

For a decrease,

$$\text{percentage decrease} = \left(\frac{\text{actual decrease}}{\text{original value}}\right) \times 100$$

Percentage profit or loss are calculated in the same way, changing
the words 'increase' to 'profit' and 'decrease' to 'loss'.

For the car above, percentage increase $= \left(\dfrac{100}{8000}\right) \times 100$

$$= 1\tfrac{1}{4}\%$$

For the speakers, percentage increase $= \left(\dfrac{100}{200}\right) \times 100 = 50\%$

(a) Waitrose reduce the price of their
own label cheesecake from £1·60 to
£1·12.
Find the percentage decrease.

The actual decrease = £0·48

Percentage decrease $= \left(\dfrac{0·48}{1·60}\right) \times 100$

$$= 30\%$$

(b) The owner of a sports shop buys tennis
rackets for £32 and sells them for
£69·99.
Find the percentage profit.

The actual profit = £37·99.

Percentage profit $= \left(\dfrac{37·99}{32}\right) \times 100$

$$= 118·7\% \text{ (1 d.p.)}$$

Exercise 3

Give answers correct to 1 decimal place, where necessary.

1. Find the percentage increase when the price of a house goes up from £120 000 to £144 000.

2. Vijay's wages were increased from £115 per week to £130 per week. What was the percentage increase?

3. Calculate the percentage increase or decrease in each case.

	Original price	Final price
(a)	£160	£176
(b)	£200	£206
(c)	£410	£630
(d)	£240	£210
(e)	$880	$836
(f)	£22·50	$18·00

4. Karim buys a car for £430 from 'Dodgy Motors Ltd'. 4 weeks later it fails its M.O.T. and he sells it for scrap rather than pay for it to be repaired. Find his percentage loss if the scrap value is £60.

5. Find either the percentage profit or loss, correct to the nearest whole number.
(a) old price = £70, new price = £105
(b) old price = £40, new price = £75
(c) old price = £90, new price = £52
(d) old price = £190, new price = £152

6. The 'Greasy Spoon' cafe buys its ingredients at the costs shown below, and then charges according to the menu. Find the percentage profit on each item.

	Item	Bought for	Menu price
(a)	Can of Cola	15p	50p
(b)	Portion of chips	8p	60p
(c)	Burger	40p	£1·20
(d)	Cup of tea	5p	40p

7. A man bought a car in an auction for £6350 and then quickly sold it for £7295. Calculate the percentage profit.

8.

Timely arrival

Elaine Donnellan gave birth to a daughter on the day that she and her husband, Richard, share as a birthday. The couple, of Chipping, Norton, Oxfordshire, won £100 from a £10 bet that Alice would arrive on March 23.

Read the newspaper article. Calculate the percentage profit made on the £10 bet.

9. In January the greatest weight a weightlifter could manage was 155 kg. After feeding on a special diet of raw meat and raw fish, he managed to lift 168 kg. Work out the percentage improvement in his performance.

10. A box has a square base of side 20 cm and height 10 cm. Calculate the percentage increase in the volume of the box after the length and width of the base are both increased by 20% and the height is increased by 15%.

11. The receptionist at a bank earns £14 200 per year and the chairman of the bank earns £315 600 per year.
   (a) Calculate the actual increase in each person's pay if they are given a 4% pay rise.
   (b) The chairman decided to take only the same actual increase as the receptionist. Calculate the percentage increase in his pay when he did this.

12. A sports centre recorded the number of girls and boys who were admitted in 2002 and 2003.

	2002	2003	Total
Girls	22 414	20 904	43 318
Boys	18 715	27 404	46 119
Total	41 129	48 308	89 437

   (a) What was the percentage increase in the number of boys admitted between 2002 and 2003?
   (b) What was the overall percentage increase in admissions between 2002 and 2003?

Reverse percentages

After an increase of 4%, the price of a railway season ticket is £998·40. What was the price before the increase?

A common mistake here is to work out 4% of £998·40. This is wrong because the increase is 4% of the *old price*, not 4% of the new price.

104% of the old price = £998·40

∴   1% of the old price = $\dfrac{998\cdot40}{104}$

∴   100% of the old price = $\dfrac{998\cdot40}{104} \times 100$

The old price = £960

Exercise 4

1. After an increase of 7%, the price of a squash racket is £58·85. Find the price of the racket before the increase.

2. After being heated, the volume of a metal ingot is increased by 3%. Find the volume of the unheated ingot, if the volume after being heated is $463\cdot5\,\text{cm}^3$.

3. After a 75% pay rise, the salary of the chairman of British Gas was £441 000. What was his salary before the increase?

4. Find the missing prices.

Item	Old price	New price	% change
(a) Lipstick	?	£7·70	10% increase
(b) Shoes	?	£42	5% increase
(c) Dress	?	£36·40	4% increase
(d) Plane ticket	?	£42	20% increase

5. As it descends, ballast is rapidly thrown overboard from a hot air balloon to reduce its weight by 3%. After the ballast is thrown the weight is 339·5 kg. Find the weight of the balloon before.

138

6. Between 1980 and 1990 the population of a town fell by 4%. Find the population of the town in 1980 if it was 252 960 in 1990.

7. In a restaurant V.A.T., at 17·5%, is added to the cost of a meal. The total cost of a meal is £42·30 including V.A.T. Find the cost of the meal before the V.A.T. was added.

8. Tescos have a special offer on its own brand pizza. Find the missing number.

35% extra FREE

432 g for the price of

9. Compared to last year, the number of cars on the roads went up by 3·2%. This corresponded to an increase of 635 200 cars. How many cars were on the roads last year?

10. In 1995 the prison population was 2% higher than in the previous year. What was the prison population in 1994, if the increase was 1040 prisoners?

11. Businessmen use the '747 Rule' to work out the V.A.T. at $17\frac{1}{2}$% which has been added to give the total price of goods. The rule to find the V.A.T. is 'Multiply by 7 and divide by 47'.

(a) Use the rule to calculate the V.A.T. on a CD which cost £112·80, including V.A.T.
(b) Check that the rule works by calculating $17\frac{1}{2}$% of the price without the V.A.T.

4.5 Trial and improvement

Exercise 1

Find the answers to these questions by trying different numbers until you find the dimensions that give the required area.

1. In the 3 rectangles below, the length is *twice* the width. Find the dimensions of each rectangle.

(a)

area = 98 cm^2

(b)

area = 12.5 cm^2

(c)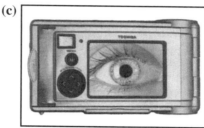

area = 9.68 cm^2

2. In these rectangles, the length is *three* times the width. Find the dimensions of each rectangle.

(a)

area = 48 cm^2

(b)

area = 36.75 cm^2

(c)

area = 3.63 cm^2

3. In the rectangle below, the length is *1 cm greater* than the width. Find the dimensions of each rectangle.

(a)

area = 72 cm^2

(b)

area = 210 cm^2

(c)

area = 60.59 cm^2

4. The volume of the box is given by the formula $n(n - 1)(n + 1)$.
   The box has a volume of $10\,626 \, \text{cm}^3$.
   Find the dimensions of the box.

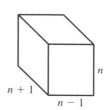

In the questions in the last exercise, we could always find dimensions which gave the *exact* answer required. In many problems this is not the case and we have to give the answer as an approximate value. This is not a major drawback because the solution can generally be found correct to as many decimal places as are required.

The rectangle shown has width h cm, length $(h + 5)$ and area 525 cm². Find the value of h, giving your answer in the form:

'h is between _____ and _____'.

The two numbers to be found differ by 0.01 [e.g. 3·61 and 3·62]

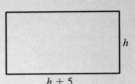

The equation to be solved is $h(h + 5) = 525$.

Try $h = 15$: $15 \times 20 = 300$, $h = 15$ is too small.
Try $h = 25$: $25 \times 30 = 750$, $h = 25$ is too large.
Try $h = 20$: $20 \times 25 = 500$, $h = 20$ is too small.
Try $h = 21$: $21 \times 26 = 546$, $h = 21$ is too large.
Try $h = 20·5$: $20·5 \times 25·0 = 522·75$, $h = 20·5$ is too small.
Try $h = 20·6$: $20·6 \times 25·6 = 527·36$, $h = 20·6$ is too large.
Try $h = 20·55$: $20·55 \times 25·55 = 525·0525$, $h = 20·55$ is too large.
Try $h = 20·54$: $20·54 \times 25·54 = 524·5916$, $h = 20·54$ is too small.

When $h = 20·55$, the area of the rectangle is greater than 525 cm² and when $h = 20·54$, the area of the rectangle is less than 525 cm².

Answer: The value of h is between 20·54 and 20·55.

Exercise 2

1. The picture shown has width h cm, length $(h + 1)$ cm and area 200 cm².
   You need to find h so that $h(h + 1) = 200$.
   Between which *one decimal place* numbers does h lie?
   Write your answer as 'h is between _____ and _____'.

   Here is the start of the solution:

   Try $h = 10$: $10 \times 11 = 110$ too small
   Try $h = 20$: $20 \times 21 = 420$ too large
   Try $h = 15$: $15 \times 16 = 240$ too large
   Try $h = 14$:   etc

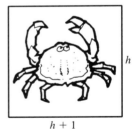

2. Find the value of h for each rectangle. Give your answer in the form: 'h is between _____ and _____', where the two numbers to be found differ by 0·1.

   (a)

   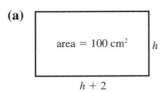

   (b)

   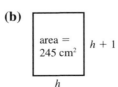

3. Solve the equations below. Give your answers in the form 'x is between _____ and _____', where the two numbers to be found differ by 0·1.

(a) $x(x + 10) = 210$ (b) $x^2 + x = 300$ (c) $x(x - 1) = 100$

Accuracy

In the last exercise the answers were given in the form 'h is between 20·54 and 20·55'.
Sometimes it is more convenient to give a solution which is correct to a specific degree of accuracy, like 2 decimal places.

In the example below, the answer is found correct to 2 decimal places.

Solve the equation $z(z - 2) = 50$, giving the answer correct to 2 decimal places.

(a) Try different values for z.

$z = 10$:	$10(10 - 2) = 80$	Too large
$z = 8$:	$8(8 - 2) = 48$	Too small
$z = 8·1$:	$8·1(8·1 - 2) = 49·41$	Too small
$z = 8·2$:	$8·2 \times 6·2 = 50·84$	Too large
$z = 8·13$:	$8·13 \times 6·13 = 49·83$	Too small
$z = 8·14$:	$8·14 \times 6·14 = 49·996$	Too small
$z = 8·15$:	$8·15 \times 6·15 = 50·1225$	Too large

(b) At this stage we know that the answer is between 8·14 and 8·15. We also note that the value of $z = 8·14$ gave the value closest to 50. [i.e. 49·996]
(c) We can take the solution to be $x = 8·14$, correct to 2 decimal places.
(d) Notes: (i) We have tried values of x just above and just below 8·14 [namely 8·15 and 8·13].
 (ii) Strictly speaking, to ensure that our answer *is* correct to 2 decimal places, we should try $x = 8·145$. This degree of complexity is unnecessary at this stage.

Solve the equation $x^3 + 10x = 100$, giving the answer correct to one decimal place.

Try $x = 3$: $3^3 + (10 \times 3) = 57$ $x = 3$ is too small.
Try $x = 4$: $4^3 + (10 \times 4) = 104$ $x = 4$ is too large.
Try $x = 3·9$: $3·9^3 + (10 \times 3·9) = 98·318$ $x = 3·9$ is too small.

Now 98·318 is closer to 100 than 104.
$\therefore$ The solution is $x = 3·9$, correct to 1 decimal place.

142

Exercise 3

1. Find the value of h, correct to 1 decimal place.

(a)

area = 738 cm² h

$h + 10$

(b)

area = 200 cm² h

$h + 5$

2. Solve the equations, correct to 1 decimal place.

(a) $x^2 + x = 13$ (b) $x^2 - x = 80$ (c) $x^3 - x = 70$

3. Use trial and improvement to find the cube root of 60, correct to 2 decimal places.

The cube root of 60 is written $\sqrt[3]{60}$.

Here is the start of the method:

Try 3: $3 \times 3 \times 3 = 27$ too small
Try 4: $4 \times 4 \times 4 = 64$ too big
Try 3.5:   etc

4. Use trial and improvement to find these roots, correct to 2 d.p.

(a) $\sqrt[3]{150}$ (b) $\sqrt[3]{58}$ (c) $\sqrt[3]{84}$ (d) $\sqrt{90}$ $\left[\begin{array}{l}\text{square root} \\ \text{not cube root}\end{array}\right]$

5. A cuboid has a square base of side x cm, height $(x + 1)$ cm and volume 2000 cm³.
Find the value of x, correct to 2 d.p.

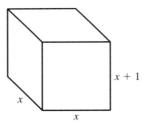

$x + 1$

x

x

6. Find a solution to the equation $4x + 1 = x^2$. Try values of x between $x = 1$ and $x = 6$.
Give your answer correct to 2 d.p. [Hint: write $x^2 - 4x = 1$]

7. In this question we require much greater accuracy. The area of the picture is 40 cm². Find the value of h correct to *five* decimal places.

h

$h + 1$

8. The 'L' shaped card shown has an area of $45\,\text{cm}^2$. Find the value of x, correct to 2 decimal places.

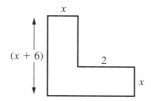

9. So far, you have solved equations involving powers of x like x^2 or x^3. Solve the equations below where numbers are raised to the power x. Give your answers correct to 1 decimal place.

(a) $3^x = 10$ (b) $12^x = 100$ (c) $7^x = 0.1$

(d) This time a number x is raised to the power x.
Solve the equation $x^x = 150$.

10. A rectangle has length $(x+2)\,\text{cm}$, perimeter $(4x+6)\,\text{cm}$ and area $52\,\text{cm}^2$.
(a) Using the perimeter, find an expression for the width of the rectangle.
(b) Form an equation, using the area, and solve it to find the value of x, correct to 2 decimal places.

11. The large triangle is an enlargement of the small triangle. Form an equation in x and solve it, giving your answer correct to 1 decimal place.

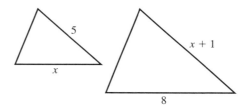

12. A window is in the shape of a semicircle joined to a rectangle. Find the radius of the semicircle, correct to 1 decimal place, if the total area of the window is $12\,\text{m}^2$.

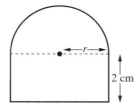

Trial and improvement using a spreadsheet

This section is written for use with Microsoft Excel. Other spreadsheet programs work in a similar way. A spreadsheet can be used to solve an equation by trial and improvement.

Select Microsoft Excel from the desk top.

A spreadsheet appears on your screen as a grid with rows numbered 1, 2, 3, 4,...... and the columns lettered A, B, C, D, ...
The result should be a window like the one below.

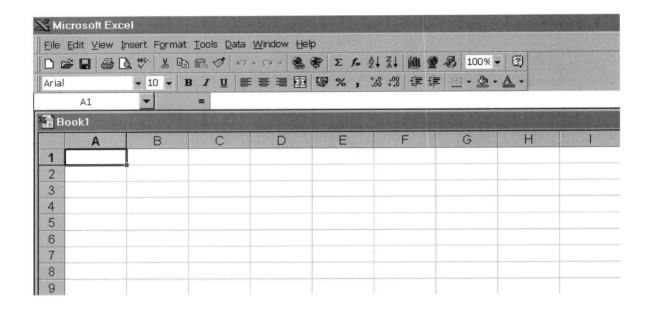

Cell   The spaces on the spreadsheet are called cells. Individual cells are referred to as A1, B3, F9, like grid references. Cells may contain *labels, values* or *formulas*. The current cell has a black border.

Label   Any words, headings or messages used to help the layout and organisation of the spreadsheet.

Value   A number placed in a cell. It may be used as input to a calculation.

Task 1.   To generate the whole numbers from 1 to 10 in column A.

(a) In cell A1 type '1' and press *Return*. This will automatically take you to the cell below. (NOTE that you must use the *Return* button and not the arrow keys to move down the column.)

(b) In cell A2 type the formula '= A1 + 1' and press *Return*. [NOTE that the = sign is needed before any formula.]

Task 1
provides practice
in using a
spreadsheet.

(c) We now want to copy the formula in A2 down column A as far as A10. Click on A2 again and put the arrow in the bottom right corner of cell A2 (a + sign will appear) and drag down to A10.

Task 2. Use trial and improvement to find an approximate solution to the equation $x^2 + x = 50$.

(a) In A1 put a label 'X VALUE'. (press *Return*).

(b) Generate the numbers from 1 to 10 in cells A2 to A11.

(c) In B1 put a label 'X * X + X'. (press *Return*) (use * for multiply).

(d) In B2 type the formula '= A2 * A2 + A2'.

(e) Copy the formula down as far as B11.

We are looking for the number nearest to 50 in the B column.
We see that B7 = 42 and B8 = 56.
We need to get a more accurate solution.
We are going to get the numbers 6·1, 6·2, 6·3, ... 6·9 in column A as follows

(f) Highlight cells A8 to B16 (9 rows).

(g) Click on 'Insert' on the tool bar and then 'Rows'.

(h) In A8 type the formula '= A7 + 0·1'.

(i) Copy the formula down as far as A16.

(j) Copy from B7 down to B16.

The value closest to 50 is 50·16. So the approximate solution to the equation $x^2 + x = 50$ is $x = 6·6$ correct to 1 decimal place.

For even greater accuracy you can repeat steps (f) to (j) starting now at A13.

Highlight cells A13 to B21 (9 rows).

Click on 'Insert' and then 'Rows'.

In A13 type '= A12 + 0·01'.

Copy the formula down to A21.

Copy from B12 down to B21.

The solution is $x = 6·59$ correct to 2 decimal places.

4.6 Puzzles and problems

Puzzles

1. The totals for the rows and columns are given. Find the values of the letters.

(a)

B	C	A	A	37
C	C	C	C	44
D	A	D	A	●
A	B	B	A	37
35	40	35	32	

(b)

T	S	T	R	T	27
P	Q	S	R	T	36
T	R	T	R	T	26
S	P	R	R	P	47
T	T	S	R	R	35
25	36	36	50	24	

(c)

X	Z	Y	W	50
Z	Y	X	X	48
Y	Y	Y	Y	48
W	Y	X	Z	50
50	46	50	32	

(d)

A	B	A	B	40
A	B	A	A	42
A	B	B	A	40
B	A	A	B	40
42	38	42	40	

2. Fill in the space in words so that it is correct:
'*This sentence has* _____ *letters.*'

3. Show how the cross can be cut along the broken lines and the pieces rearranged to make a square.

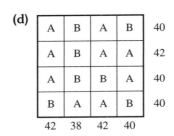

4. Replace the boxes with three mathematical symbols
(+, −, ×, ÷) so that the calculation is correct.

(105 ☐ 7) ☐ 3 ☐ 7 = 38

5. For this multiplying box, there are
five *outside* numbers [5, 7, 11, 2, 9]
and
six *inside* numbers [10, 14, 22, 45, 63, 99].

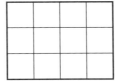

Draw a 4 × 3 box and position the
seven outside numbers [26, 45, 11,
15, 9, 33, 22] and the twelve inside
numbers [495, 99, 572, 135, 286,
990, 390, 495, 675, 363, 198, 726]
so that the box works like the one
above.

6. A lottery prize of £5555 was shared equally between a number
of people so that each person received a whole number of
pounds. There were between 20 and 100 people. How many
people shared the prize and how much did each person
receive?

7. A double-decker bus
has just 10 seats.
There are 5 seats in
a line upstairs and 5
downstairs.

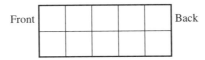

Dave is sitting directly below Karen and in front of eight
people. Philip is sitting right at the back, directly above Neha.
Lisa is directly in front of Greg and directly above Richard.
Chris is just behind Jim and directly below Bob.
Who is directly behind Karen?

8. The diagram on the right is the net of a cube made from
cardboard.
Which of the six cubes below could not be made from this net?

net

A

B

C

D

E

F

9. The symbols $*$, $\bigcirc$, $\triangle$, $\square$ represent weights. Use the information in (i), (ii), (iii) to answer part (iv).

(a) (i) $* + \triangle = \square$

(ii) $* = \triangle + \bigcirc$

(iii) $* + * + \triangle = \square + \bigcirc + \bigcirc$

(iv) $\triangle$ = How many $\bigcirc$'s?

(b) (i) $\bigcirc + \bigcirc + \square = * + \bigcirc$

(ii) $* + * = \bigcirc + \bigcirc + \bigcirc$

(iii) $\square + * = \bigcirc + \bigcirc$

(iv) $*$ = How many $\square$'s?

S.M.C Questions

The questions below are taken from past School Mathematics Challenge papers. They are reproduced here with the kind permission of Dr Tony Gardiner of the U.K. Mathematics Foundation, Birmingham.

1. Weighing the baby at the clinic was a problem. The baby would not keep still and caused the scales to wobble. So I held the baby and stood on the scales while the nurse read off 78 kg. Then the nurse held the baby while I read off 69 kg. Finally I held the nurse while the baby read off 137 kg. What would the combined weight of nurse, baby and me be (in kilograms)?

(a) 142   (b) 147   (c) 206   (d) 215   (e) 284

2. Baby's nearly 1 now. We've worked out how to weigh her, but nurse and I still have trouble measuring her height. She just *will* not stand up straight against our measuring chart. In fact she can't stand up at all yet! So we measure her upside down. Last year nurse held Baby's feet, keeping them level with the 140 cm mark, while I read off the mark level with the top of Baby's head: 97 cm. This year it was my turn to hold the feet. Being taller than nurse I held them against the 150 cm mark while nurse crawled on the floor to read the mark level with the top of Baby's head: 84 cm. How many centimetres has Baby grown in her first year?

(a) 13   (b) 237   (c) 53   (d) 23   (e) 66

3. Baby's 2 now and drinks milk by the quarter pint, so we have decided to call her GILL. Getting her to recognise her name proved difficult, so we put the four letters G, I, L, L on separate building blocks. She loves arranging them, but rarely gets them in the right order. One day she managed to produce every possible four-letter 'word' (L I L G is one such). How many different four-letter words did she produce that day?

(a) 3   (b) 4   (c) 12   (d) 16   (e) 24

4. Gill's back! This year, was her fourth birthday. The highlight of her party was a game of musical chairs. The game got down to herself, nurse, and me. Only two chairs were left – the hard chair and the comfy chair, with a big gap between them. The music stopped and we all piled onto the nearest chair, some on top of one another. If Gill's bottom was firmly in contact with one of the two chairs, in how many different ways could this have happened?

(a) 4   (b) 6   (c) 8   (d) 10   (e) 12

5. Gill has now started primary skool and is learning to spell. We got her to help by writing out this queschun for us. We gave her a score of 100 to start with, and deducted 10% of her running total each time we found a word spelt rong. What was her final score?

(a) 70   (b) 72·9   (c) 80   (d) 81   (e) 90

6. Gill is just six and boasts that she can count up to 100. However, she often mixes up nineteen and ninety, and so jumps straight from nineteen to ninety one. How many numbers does she miss out when she does this?

(a) 70   (b) 71   (c) 72   (d) 78   (e) 89

7. Gill arranges the fingers of her right hand so that her thumb points upwards, her first finger points north and her second finger points west: we write this for short as "TU, 1N, 2W". She then keeps her fingers fixed like this, but can twist her arm and her wrist if she likes. Which of the following arrangements can she *not* achieve? (D = down, S = south, E = east.)

(a) TD, 1N, 2E   (b) TN, 1D, 2W   (c) TS, 1E, 2U
(d) TE, 1U, 2S   (e) TW, 1S, 2D

Part 5

5.1 Averages and range

Exercise 1

1. (a) Find the mean of the numbers   3, 2, 7, 8, 11
   (b) Find the median of the numbers   8, 5, 3, 1, 4, 3, 9
   (c) Find the mode of the numbers   4, 3, 4, 4, 3, 2, 4, 3

2. Write a sentence which describes how you would find the median of a set of nine numbers.

3. Find the range of each set of numbers
   (a) 5, 2, 11, 25, 7, 10
   (b) 2, 2, 2, 2, 2, 2, 2
   (c) 8, 0, −3, 6, 15, 7

4. For the set of numbers below, find the mean and the median.

0,   0,   1,   1,   1,   2,   51

   Which average best describes this set of numbers? Explain why.

5. In a medieval jousting competition, marks were awarded for gallantry, courage, skill and so on using the 'Agincourt Scale'.
   Prince Gibson scored marks of 0, 0, 0, −2, 1, −5.
   What was his mean score?

6. Duncan has three test results with a mean of 25 and a range of 20. His first result was 21.
   What did he get on the other two tests?

7. Prini has 5 cards. The 5 cards have a mean of 11 and a range of 8.
   What are the numbers on the last two cards?

8. Chloe and Joanne compared their marks in five subjects.

	English	Mathematics	French	Science	History
Chloe	35	42	53	45	50
Joanne	33	48	52	x	41

If the mean of the five subjects is the same for both girls calculate the missing mark for Science.

9. Carla needs a mean score of 70% or more over her four examination papers. Her mean for the first three papers is 68%. What is the minimum she needs to score on her final paper?

10. Philip has three dart scores with a median score of 36 and a mean score of 32. The range of the three scores is 20. What are the three scores?

11. The mean height of 10 people is 150 cm. One person of height 141 cm leaves the group. Find the mean height of the remaining nine people.

12. The masses of 20 stones are given in the table.

mass	5 g	8 g	9 g	10 g
number of stones	7	4	7	2

Find the mean mass of the stones.

13. The marks achieved by 30 grandmothers in a football quiz were as follows:

mark	1	2	3	4	5
frequency	4	7	7	9	3

Find   (a) the mean mark
        (b) the median mark
        (c) the modal mark

14. The following table gives the heights achieved by two club athletes in the high jump.

Mike	178	181	179	182	181	180	170
Neil	180	172	175	180	184	182	185

(a) Calculate the mean and range for each jumper.
(b) Which person should a selector choose to represent the club? Explain your decision by referring to the mean and the range.

15. Here are five cards, written in terms of n, which is a whole number.

$$n + 2 \qquad n - 2$$
$$2n + 4$$
$$5n + 7 \qquad n + 4$$

(a) Find, in terms of n,
  (i) the range of the five cards
  (ii) the median of the five cards
  (iii) the mean of the five cards

(b) The mean is 3 greater than the median. Find the value of n.

Stem and leaf diagrams

Exercise 2

1. (a) Here are the marks of 13 pupils in a spelling test:

41 32 50 44 62 68 71 54 47 35 68 55 56

(b) The results are shown on a stem and leaf diagram.
(c) What was the median mark?

Stem (tens)	Leaf (units)			
3	2	5		
4	1	4	7	
5	0	4	5	6
6	2	8	8	
7	1			

Key $3|2 = 32$

2. Here is the stem and leaf diagram showing the weights, in pounds, of animals in a pet shop.

(a) Write down the range of the masses.
(b) How many animals were in the shop?
(c) What is the median weight?

Stem	Leaf			
1	2	5	8	
2	1	3		
3	2	7	8	8
4	5	6		

$1|2$ means 12

3. The stem and leaf diagram shows
the number of points scored by a
local rugby team
(a) How many games were played?
(b) Find the range of the points scored.

Stem	Leaf
1	2 2 5 7 8
2	1 2 2 4 4 4 7 8
3	1 2 3 3 4 5
4	4 4 6 8 8
5	1

Key 1|2 = 12 points

4. Here are two stem and leaf diagrams showing the marks of
children in two tests, Maths and Science.

Maths:

Stem	Leaf
2	8
3	3 4 5 8
4	2 4 7 7 9
5	1

Key 2|8 = 28

Science:

Stem	Leaf
2	1 2 5
3	6 7
4	5 6
5	5 7
6	3 8

(a) What was the median mark for each test?
(b) What was the range for each test?
(c) In which test were the marks spread out more widely?

5. The masses of 20 apples from a tree were recorded to the nearest
gram. Illustrate the data on a stem and leaf diagram and find
the median mass.

123 134 121 126 127 135 136 138 140 132
124 143 139 120 137 133 136 122 141 134

Stem	Leaf
12	3 . . . . . .
13	. . . .
14	. . . .

6. Some pupils took tests in Maths and English. Their scores are
shown in the back-to-back stem and leaf diagram.

(a) Find the median and
range for Maths.

(b) Find the median and
range for English.

(c) Write a sentence to
compare the two sets
of data.

Maths	Stem	English
7 6	1	3
8 5	2	2 3 6 8
2 2 1	3	1 4 6 7 7 9
7 7 3	4	2 2 4 5 6 6 9
8 6 5 5 3	5	3 5 6 6 7 8 8 8
8 4 3 2	6	1 1 4
6 2 1 1 1	7	2
7 4 3	8	
8 6 3	9	

6|1 = 16%

1|3 = 13%

5.2 Drawing graphs

In Book 8i we used flow diagrams to find the coordinates of points on a graph. In this section we work directly from the equation of the graph to find the coordinates of the points.

To draw the line $y = 2x - 1$, we begin by working out the y values for different values of x. In this case we take x from -2 to $+3$.

when $x = -2$, $y = 2 \times (-2) - 1 = -5$

$x = -1$, $y = 2 \times (-1) - 1 = -3$

$x = 0$, $y = 2 \times (0) - 1 = -1$

$x = 1$, $y = 2 \times (1) - 1 = 1$

$x = 2$, $y = 2 \times (2) - 1 = 3$

$x = 3$, $y = 2 \times (3) - 1 = 5$

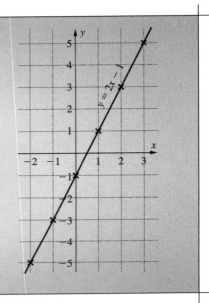

The points $(-2, -5)$, $(-1, -3)$ ... $(3, 5)$ are plotted and a line is drawn through them.

Exercise 1

For each question, work out the y values for the range of x values given. Draw the graph, using a scale of 1 cm to 1 unit on both axes.

1. $y = 3x + 1$; take x from 0 to 4.
   Continue this working:
   when $x = 0$, $y = (3 \times 0) + 1 = 1$
   $x = 1$, $y = (3 \times 1) + 1 = 4$
   $\vdots$

   Draw the graph using a scale of 1 cm to 1 unit on both axes.

2. $y = 2x - 3$; take x from 1 to 5.
   when $x = 1$, $y = (2 \times 1) - 3 = -1$
   $x = 2$, $y = (2 \times 2) - 3 = 1$
   $\vdots$

3. $y = x - 1$; take x from 0 to 6.

4. $y = 2x + 2$; take x from -2 to $+4$.

5. $y = 3x - 2$; take x from -2 to $+3$.

6. $y = x + 5$; take x from -3 to $+3$.

7. $y = 4x - 1$; take x from -2 to $+3$. Use scales of 1 cm to 1 unit on the x axis and 1 cm to 2 units on the y axis.

8. $y = 3x + 2$; take x from -3 to $+3$. Use the scales given in Question **7**.

9. (a) Consider the graph of $x + y = 20$.
     We can rearrange the equation to make y the subject.
     Subtract x from both sides: $y = 20 - x$

   (b) Make y the subject of the equation $3x + y = 8$

   (c) Make y the subject of the equation $y - 2x = 10$

Hint:
You need
'$y = \ldots$'

10. Make y the subject of these equations:
    (a) $4x + y = 12$ (b) $y + 3x = 10$ (c) $y - x + 5 = 0$
    (d) $y - 3x - 6 = 0$ (e) $2x + y = 0$ (f) $x + 2y = 10$

In Questions **11** to **14** draw the graph. [Scale: 1 cm to 1 unit]

11. $x + y = 10$; take x from 0 to 10.

12. $x + y = 6$; take x from 0 to 6.

13. $2x + y = 10$; take x from 0 to 6.

14. $3x + 2y = 18$; take x from 0 to 5.

15. Using the same axes, draw the graphs of $y = x + 1$ and $x + y = 7$. Take values of x from 0 to 6.
    Write down the coordinates of the point where the lines meet.

16. On the same graph, draw the lines $y = 2x - 3$,
$$y = \tfrac{1}{2}x,$$
$$x + y = 9.$$
    Take values of x from 0 to 8.
    Write down the coordinates of the three vertices of the triangle formed.

17. On the same graph, draw the lines $x + y = 8$,
$$y = 2x + 2,$$
$$y = 2.$$
    Take values of x from 0 to 8.
    Find the area of the triangle formed.

156

Inverse functions

- With the function $x \to 2x$ 1 is 'mapped onto' 2,
  2 is mapped onto 4,
  3 is mapped onto 6 and so on.

The *inverse* function is $x \to \dfrac{x}{2}$

- A linear function is a function whose graph is a straight line.

  For example $x \to 5x + 8$, $\qquad x \to 1 - 7x$, $\qquad x \to \dfrac{x+4}{2}$

  We can find the inverse of a linear function using a flow diagram.

Here is the flow diagram
for $x \to 3x + 2$

Now draw the flow diagram with
inverse operations.

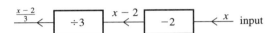

The inverse is found using x as
the input and going through the
diagram from right to left.

Here is another example.

$$x \to \boxed{+2} \xrightarrow{x+2} \boxed{\times 5} \xrightarrow{5(x+2)} \qquad \frac{x}{5}-2 \leftarrow \boxed{-2} \xleftarrow{\frac{x}{5}} \boxed{\div 5} \xleftarrow{x}$$

The inverse of $x \to 5(x + 2)$ is $x \to \dfrac{x}{5} - 2$

Exercise 2

Find the inverse function
1. $x \to 4x + 1$
2. $x \to 5x - 3$
3. $x \to 7x + 1$

4. $x \to 5(x + 7)$
5. $x \to 10(x - 4)$
6. $x \to \dfrac{x+7}{3}$

7. $x \to \dfrac{x-4}{2}$
8. $x \to \dfrac{1}{2}x - 6$
9. $x \to \dfrac{1}{3}x + 11$

10. $x \to 3(2x - 1)$
11. $x \to \dfrac{4x+1}{5}$
12. $x \to 7\left(\dfrac{1}{2}x - 5\right)$

13. Functions of the form $x \to c - x$ are *self inverse*. So the inverse
of $x \to c - x$ is the *same* function.
Find the inverse functions:

(a) $x \to 12 - x$
(b) $x \to 30 - x$.

Use different inputs to show that your answers are correct.

5.3 Ratio and map scales

Look at this plant.

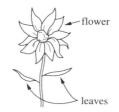

flower

leaves

As a RATIO we say 'flowers to leaves'.
flowers : leaves
=   1 : 2

Exercise 1 The Snodget.

SIDE VIEW

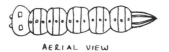

AERIAL VIEW

The Snodget is a strange creature. It is born with no middle, and no feet!

Every 7 days it grows a middle section, and 2 feet.

Important Snodget ratios,
A. Spots : Stripes
     = 3 : 2

B. Age in days : Number of sections
     = 7 : 1

The Snodget above is 35 days old.

1. How many **stripes** has a Snodget with:
   (a) 6 spots?
   (b) 9 spots?
   (c) 21 spots?

2. How many **spots** has a Snodget with:
   (a) 4 stripes?
   (b) 10 stripes?
   (c) 18 stripes?

3. How old is a Snodget when its 3rd section has grown?

4. How many sections has a 12 week old Snodget?

5. Fill in the blanks in this sentence: 'For a 12 week old Snodget the ratio, spots : stripes = _____ : _____.'

6. How many spots has a 2 week old Snodget?

7. Draw a picture of a Snodget which is 49 days old.

Simplifying ratios
A ratio can be simplified if all the numbers have a common factor.
So the ratio 2 : 6 can be simplified to the ratio 1 : 3.
The ratio 3 : 6 : 15 can be simplified to the ratio 1 : 2 : 5.

Exercise 2

Write these ratios in a more simple form.

1. 10 : 5   **2.** 4 : 6   **3.** 12 : 4   **4.** 6 : 15

5. 10 : 2   **6.** 8 : 20   **7.** 14 : 8   **8.** 16 : 20

9. 3 : 18   **10.** 12 : 9   **11.** 30 : 25   **12.** 30 : 24

13. 9 : 21   **14.** 35 : 21   **15.** 32 : 40   **16.** 49 : 56

17. 48 : 36   **18.** 2 : 4 : 8   **19.** 2 : 6 : 12   **20.** 3 : 9 : 21

Ratio and sharing

- Louise is five times hungrier than Philip.
  Share 12 sweets between Louise and Philip in the ratio 5 : 1.

Louise : Philip
= 5 : 1
Total of 6 shares

Each share = 12 ÷ 6
= 2 sweets
So Louise's share is 5 × 2 = 10 sweets
Philip's share is 1 × 2 = 2 sweets

- Share £20 between Bill and Ben in the ratio 3 : 2.

Bill : Ben
= 3 : 2
Total of 5 shares

Each share = 20 ÷ 5
= £4
So Bill's share is (3 × 4) = £12
Ben's share = (2 × 4) = £8

Exercise 3

Share these quantities in the ratios given.

1. 18 apples between Tina and Gill, ratio 2 : 1

2. 30 oranges between Rachael and Sheila, ratio 2 : 3

3. 24 pears between Robert and Peter, ratio 3 : 1

4. 35 bananas between Richard and Ron, ratio 2 : 5

5. 42 teabags between David and Jacqui, ratio 5 : 1

6. 56 rulers between X and Y, ratio 2 : 5

7. 44 pencils between M and N, ratio 7 : 4

8. 63 erasers between S and T, ratio 4 : 5

9. 77 pens between F and G, ratio 1 : 6

10. 132 mints between C and D, ratio 4 : 7

11. Find the largest share in these problems
   (a) £70, ratio 4 : 3
   (b) 180 kg, ratio 4 : 5
   (c) $225, ratio 7 : 8

12. Find the smallest share in these problems
   (a) 480 g, ratio 5 : 3
   (b) $510, ratio 12 : 5
   (c) £380, ratio 15 : 4

Exercise 4

1. In a room, the ratio of boys to girls is 2 : 3. If there are 8 boys, how many girls are there?

2. In an office the ratio of men to women is 5 : 1. If there are 30 men, how many women are there?

3. A photo was enlarged in the ratio 2 : 3. The original photo was 8 cm wide. How wide was the enlarged copy?

8 cm

original

enlarged copy

4. A photocopier enlarges copies in the ratio 3 : 5. The length of a shark was 12 cm on the original. How long is the shark on the enlarged copy?

5. In a hall, the ratio of chairs to tables is 7 : 2. If there are 10 tables, how many chairs are there?

6. The ratio of squash to water in a drink is 3 : 8. How much squash is used with 4 litres of water?

7. Find the ratio (shaded area) : (unshaded area) for each diagram.

(a) 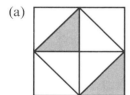   (b) 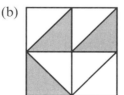   (c)

8. If $\frac{5}{8}$ of the children in a class are girls, what is the ratio of girls to boys?

9. Concrete for paths consists of cement, sand and gravel in the ratio 1 : 2 : 4 by volume. What volume of sand is needed to make 14 m^3 of concrete? Give your answer correct to 2 d.p.

10. Bread is made from flour and yeast in the ratio 30 to 1.
   (a) How much yeast is mixed with 960 g of flour?
   (b) How much flour is needed to mix with 400 g of yeast?

11. A prize of £50 000 is shared between Ken, Len and Ben in the ratio 2 : 3 : 5. How much does each person receive?

12. Divide 6000 g of gold between three prospectors in the ratio 3 : 4 : 5.

13. Lee, Mike and Neil formed a syndicate to enter a giant lottery. They agreed to share their winnings in the ratio of their contributions. Lee paid £1, Mike paid 60p and Neil paid 25p. Together they won £1 480 000. How much did Neil get?

14. The diagram shows 3 squares A, B and C. The sides of the squares are in the ratio 1 : 3 : 6.

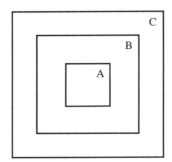

   (a) The side of square B is 9 cm. Find the sides of square A and the sides of square C.

   (b) Write this ratio in its simplest form, side of square B : side of square C

   (c) Work out the areas of squares A and C

   (d) Write this ratio, in its simplest form area of square A : area of square C.

Map scales

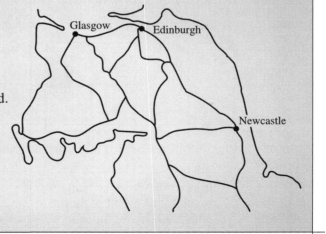

On a map of scale 1 : 3 000 000, Edinburgh and Newcastle appear 5 cm apart. What is the actual distance between the towns?

1 cm on map = 3 000 000 cm on land.
5 cm on map = 5 × 3 000 000 cm on land.
15 000 000 cm = 150 000 m
            = 150 km
Edinburgh is 150 km from Newcastle.

Exercise 5

1. On a map whose scale is 1 : 100 000, the distance between two villages is 7 cm. What is the actual distance in kilometres between the two villages?

2. Two towns are 9 cm apart on a map whose scale is 1 : 5 000 000. Find the actual distance between the two towns.

3. On a map whose scale is 1 : 200 000 the distance between two towns is 8·5 cm. Find the actual distance between the towns.

4. A river is 3 cm long on a map whose scale is 1 : 50 000. Find the actual length of the river.

5. The scale of a map is 1 : 10 000. Find the actual length in metres of a road which is 2 cm long on the map.

6. The distance between two towns is 20 km. How far apart will they be on a map of scale 1 : 4000?

7. The length of a lake is 2 km. How long will it be on a map of scale 1 : 100 000?

8. The distance between two points is 30 km. How far apart will they be on a map of scale 1 : 50 000?

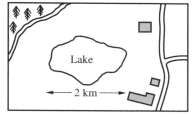

1 : 100 000

9. The length of a section of motorway is 15 km. How long will it be on a map of scale 1 : 100 000?

10. Copy and complete the table

Map scale	Actual length on land	Length on map
(a) 1 : 5000	4 km	cm
(b) 1 : 20 000	52 km	cm
(c) 1 : 80 000	20 km	cm
(d) 1 : 10 000	84 km	cm

11. The scale of a drawing is 1 cm to 5 m. The length of a wall is 20 m. What length will the wall be on the drawing?

5.4 Mixed problems 2

Exercise 1

1. How many stamps each costing 31p can be bought for £5?

2. A typist is paid £6·20 per hour. How much does she earn in a week when she works 40 hours?

3. It needs 100 g of flour to make 20 small cakes. How much flour is needed to make 8 of these cakes?

4. A car uses 15 litres of fuel for every 100 km travelled. Calculate the cost, in £, of travelling 300 km if petrol costs 62p per litre.

5. Between the times 15·48 and 16·18 the mileometer of a car changes from 28 793 miles to 28 825 miles. At what average speed is the car travelling?

6. A rectangular box, without a lid, is to be made from cardboard.
   (a) What is the volume of the box?
   (b) Draw a net of the box.
   (c) What area of cardboard is required?

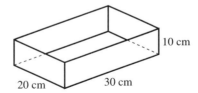

7. A jet is flying at 720 km/h.
   (a) How many metres will it travel in one hour?
   (b) How many metres will it travel in one second?

8.
   A large wheel in a machine turns once every 10 seconds. How many rotations will it make in 2 hours?

9. Nine bars of chocolate weigh 432 g. They cost £4·95 altogether.
   (a) How much does one bar weigh?
   (b) How much does one bar cost?
   (c) How many bars can I buy for £7·15?

10. Copy and complete this multiplication square.

×	5	3		
		12		36
			14	
8	40			
			42	54

Exercise 2

1.

To watch Sheringham and Klinsman, 36 550 Spurs fans paid an average ticket price of £37·50.
How much money was paid for tickets altogether?

2. The cost of advertising in a local paper for one week is

28p per word plus 75p

(a) What is the cost of an advertisement of 15 words for one week?
(b) What is the greatest number of words in an advertisement costing up to £8 for one week?

3. Find the missing digits

(a) $\boxed{}\,7 \times 1\,\boxed{} = 611$

(b)
```
      3 6 6
  8)□ 9 □ 8
```

(c) $\boxed{}\,6 \times 1\,\boxed{} = 442$

(d)
```
    6 □ 1
  − □ 7 □
    ─────
    2 6 3
```

(e)
```
    □ □ 5
  ×     9
    ─────
    2 5 6 □
```

(f)
```
        4 8 3
  7)□ 3 □ 1
```

4. (a) Find two consecutive numbers which multiply together to give 240.
(b) Find three consecutive numbers which multiply together to give 10 626.

5. A 20p coin is 1·2 mm thick. What is the value of a pile of 20p coins which is 21·6 cm high?

6. Work out $\frac{3}{5} + 0.12 + \frac{3}{4}$, and write the answer as a decimal.

7. Work out, without using a calculator
    (a) 0·4 − 0·04   (b) 0·03 × 1000   (c) 0·31 ÷ 10
    (d) 8·7 − 4   (e) 3% of £500   (f) $\sqrt{(11{\cdot}38 + 13{\cdot}62)}$

8. Write correct to the nearest pound:
    (a) £57·80   (b) £62·45   (c) £124·85
    (d) £6·781   (e) £11·382   (f) £567·60

9. 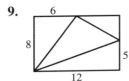 A rectangle is divided into four triangles as shown. Find the area of the biggest of the triangles.

10. A garden 9 m by 12 m is to be treated with fertilizer. One cup of fertilizer covers an area of 3 m² and one bag of fertilizer is sufficient for 18 cups.
    (a) Find the area of the garden.
    (b) Find the number of bags of fertilizer needed.

11.  A prize-winning sand castle was built by 15 people in ten hours.
How long would it take 4 people to build the sand castle if they worked at the same speed and with equal skill?

Exercise 3

1. Find the missing digits

(a)
$$\begin{array}{r} \square\,4\,\square \\ +\ 1\,\square\,8 \\ \hline 4\,1\,4 \end{array}$$

(b)
$$\begin{array}{r} \square\,\square\,9 \\ \times\quad 4 \\ \hline 1\ 3\ 9\ \square \end{array}$$

(c) $\square\,4 \times 2\,\square = 1512$

2. Andrew left his home at 7.35 a.m. and drove at an average speed of 44 m.p.h. arriving at the airport at 8.05 a.m. How far is his home from the airport?

3. The perimeter of a rectangle is 22 cm. Find the width of the rectangle if its length is 8 cm.

4.

Dinky's high price

A Dinky Toy model of a Bentalls Kingston-on-Thames delivery van which cost 6d (2¹/₂p) in 1936, fetched a record £12,650 at a Christie's auction.

How many of the original models at $2\frac{1}{2}$p could you buy with £12 650?

5. The diagram shows the map of a farm which grows four different crops in the regions shown.

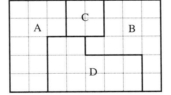

Each square represents one acre.
(a) What is the total area of the farm?
(b) What area is used for crop A?
(c) What percentage of the farm is used for crop C?
(d) What percentage of the farm is used for crop D?

6. The train fare to Dover is £5·30 for an adult and £1·60 for a child. How much change will a man get from £20 if he is taking his wife and three children?

7. The symbols ∗, ∇, □, ○ represent numbers.
Use the clues in (a) and (b) to answer part (c).
(a) $\ast + \nabla = \square$
(b) $\ast + \ast + \nabla = \square + \bigcirc + \bigcirc + \bigcirc$
(c) How many ○'s?

8. It rained so hard that a 4 cm deep egg cup was filled in 20 minutes. How much rain fell between 07:30 and 13:50? Assume it rained steadily at the same rate.

9. That's the way the money goes: used banknotes, chopped up and compressed, are dumped for the Bank of England at a landfill site near Tilbury. The bank has to dispose of seven tonnes a day. To avoid pollution they are no longer burned, but selling them as novelty firelighters is among proposals being investigated.

Estimate the value of the banknotes which are dumped each day.
Make the following assumptions:
(a) All the notes dumped are £10 notes.
(b) each note weighs 0·87 grams.
[1 tonne = 1000 kg]

10. How many points inside and outside the square are the same distance from B and C and are also 5 cm from A?

Exercise 4

1. Forty teenagers were asked to name their favourite holiday destinations with the following results:

    Spain 12, France 5, Greece 10
    Portugal 4, U.S.A. 9

   Display this information on a pie chart, showing the angles corresponding to each country.

2. (a) A rectangular floor 3 m by 4 m is to be covered with square tiles, each of side length 50 cm. How many tiles will be required?
   (b) If the same floor is covered with smaller tiles of side 25 cm, how many are needed now?

3. Use a calculator to work out 11^2, 111^2 and 1111^2. Use your answers to predict the values of $11\,111^2$ and $111\,111^2$.

4. The canoeists are concentrating on two numbers n and m. The product of n and m is 204 and their sum is 29.
   Find the two numbers.

5. At a party there are 116 people and there are 6 more boys than girls.
   How many boys are there?

6. Mark uses 14 screws in each of the model aircraft which he makes.
   How many *complete* aircraft can he make using a box of 360 screws?

7.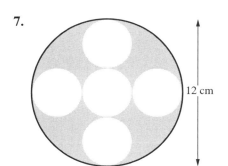

   12 cm

   Find the shaded area. Give your answer in cm^2, correct to one decimal place.

8. £1 = 8·3 French Francs.
   (a) How many Francs would you get for £100?
   (b) How much English currency is equivalent to 50 Francs?

9. To get the next number in a sequence you double the previous number and subtract two. The third number in the sequence is 50. Find the first number.

10. A code uses 1 for A, 2 for B, 3 for C and so on up to 26 for Z. Coded words are written without spaces to confuse the enemy, so 18 could be AH or R. Decode the following message.
    208919   919   1   2251825   199121225   31545

5.5 Statistical problems

What sort of problem?

In general we are concerned here with solving problems or answering questions for which data is required. Here are some examples:

- Is the R.S.P.C.A. the most popular charity in the country?
- How much T.V. do adults and children watch?
- Do first class letters arrive next day?
- Will people use trains if they are cheaper and run on time?
- Which subject do people find most difficult at school?

Many problems of a statistical nature are made more clear when they are put in the form of a *conjecture*. A conjecture is a statement which may or may not be true. Here are some examples of conjectures:

- More money is donated to the R.S.P.C.A. than to any other charity.
- People aged 18 and over watch more T.V. than under 18 year olds.
- 90% of first class letters arrive next day.

The data relevant to each problem might be obtained from:

- A questionnaire or survey of a sample of people
- Published tables or from computer databases
- The internet

Collecting data

Collecting *data* means collecting information. For your own work you might need information about, for example, time watching T.V., distance to school, height, expenditure and so on. The next section is about designing effective data collection sheets.

When you design a data collection sheet you must think ahead and decide what exactly is the purpose of the survey and what information does each question provide. Think also about the *order* of the questions.

Here are several points to consider when designing a sheet.

● Keep it as short and simple as possible.
    People are (quite rightly) not prepared to spend a long time filling in forms.

● Do not ask questions if they are not relevant.
    Do not ask for the person's name unless you have to. People are more likely to cooperate if their replies are anonymous.

● Try not to ask questions that require written replies.
    You may get a hundred different points of view which makes analysing the answers extremely difficult. It is much better to ask questions that can be answered with yes/no or by ticking an appropriate box. Do not *only* ask questions which can be answered yes/no.

● Try to avoid personal questions.
    If you ask someone their age, weight or income they will often be inclined to give you false information. A better approach would be to ask 'Which category do you fall into?'

| under 16 | 16–19 | 20–29 | 30–49 | 50 or over |

● Make sure you cover all possibilities.
    Do not leave a person thinking 'I don't belong to any of those categories'.

● Do not ask questions in such a way that the person feels forced to agree.

Example 1.   Most people would find it difficult to say 'no' to a question such as 'Don't you agree that the cruel and inhumane way of transporting live animals should be abolished'.

Example 2.   Do *not* ask: 'Do you agree that pupils in this school are given too much homework?'.

A better question is:

The amount of homework set to pupils in this school is:

Tick one box.

not enough	about right	too much	don't know

170

- Here are two data collection sheets: the first is well designed but the second contains several faults.

Good

I am collecting information to see if there is any connection between a person's height and the height of their parents.

Tell people what you are doing

1. Please tick one box — Male □ Female □

2. Age: please tick one box — 13→15 □ 16→18 □ 19 and over □

Make it easy to answer.

3. Please state your height, either in feet and inches or in cm. — height □

4. Please state the height of your father [If you are not sure an estimate will be O.K.] — height of father □

Use the word 'please' frequently.

5. Please state the height of your mother — height of mother □

Not Good

State your name and age. — Name _____ Age _____

No introduction

Not a good idea

People often don't like to state their age

- How much television do you watch on average? not much □ quite a lot □ a lot □

Much too vague

- Which are your favourite programmes on T.V.?

You may get 100 different answers. This will be impossible to analyse.

- Do you agree that BBC1 provides the best news coverage? agree □ disagree □

Question is biased towards agreeing

Needs a box for 'don't know'

Exercise 1

In Questions **1** to **6** explain why the question is not suitable for a data collection sheet. Write an improved question in each case.

1. How much do you earn per month?

   | 0–£100 | £100–£200 | £200–£500 | £400–£700 | more than £700 |

2. Wouldn't you agree that the present government is doing an appalling job?

3. For how long do you watch the television each day?

   | 2–3 hrs | 3–4 hrs | 5–6 hrs |

4. Do you think that the disintegration of theological suppositions is leading to ethical degeneration?

5. Which sort of holiday do you most enjoy?

6. Some of the money from the National Lottery goes to charities.
   Tick one box:

   The money going to charities is ☐ ☐
                                      Too little   Too much

7. A group of pupils were asked to design a questionnaire to find out people's views about watching sport on television. Comment on the following two pupils' efforts. Design an improved questionnaire to find out people's opinions.

   (a)
   ```
   Name ............ Sex M/F

   Age ................

   Do you like sport? .......... Y/N

   Do you have satellite TV? ......
                              Y/N

   Is there enough sport on TV?
                     .......... Y/N
   ```

   (b)
   Do you like sport?
   Not at all
   Not much
   A bit
   Quite a lot
   I love it

   Do you have cable or satellite TV?
   Yes/No

   How often do you watch sport?
   Every day
   Up to three times a week
   Less than twice a month

   Should there be more sport on television?
   Yes/No

8. A new variety of soup, 'Cheese and Onion', is to be launched by a leading manufacturer. They wish to know if it will be popular and sell well. People are asked to try a free sample and comment on their impression.
   Design a data collection sheet to test people's opinions.

Your own work, testing a conjecture

● A conjecture is a statement which may or may not be true.

    Examples: 'Spurs are the best team in the world.'

               'Tall people are less likely to wear glasses than short people.'

               'Most people in schools find French the hardest subject.'

               "People who are good at Maths are also good at Science.'

● A conjecture can often be tested by conducting a survey in which a large number of people respond to a questionnaire.
When you design a questionnaire you should think ahead to how you will display your results. In general, graphs or charts are easier for other people to understand than tables of numbers.

You might use:
Pie charts;
Bar charts;
Scatter graphs;
Line graphs.

 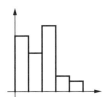 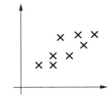 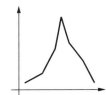

● *Do* use colour in your work and *do* write a short and clear summary of your results. Comment on whether your results support or do not support your conjecture.
Don't produce page after page of repetitive, uninteresting results without any comments or observations.

● It is always a good idea to ask a few people to try out your questions in a *pilot survey*. Then if there are any problems with the questions these can be corrected. You might also get ideas for additional questions.

● You will almost certainly design a more interesting questionnaire if *you* choose the topic or the conjecture to be tested.

5.6 Mathematical reasoning

Break the codes

1. The ten symbols below each stand for one of the digits 0, 1, 2, 3, 4, 5, 6, 7, 8, 9 but not in that order.

   $\odot \ \triangledown \ \square \ * \ \uparrow \ ? \ \ominus \ \pi \ \mp \ I$

   Use the clues below to work out what number each symbol stands for.

   (a) $* + * = ?$
   (b) $\triangledown \times \triangledown = \ominus$
   (c) $? + ? + ? = \odot$
   (d) $\square - * = \odot$
   (e) $\pi + I = \ominus$
   (f) $\pi \times \uparrow = \uparrow$
   (g) $\mp - I = I$

2. The ten symbols used in part 1 are used again but with different values.
   The clues are more difficult to work out.

   (a) $\ominus + \mp = I$
   (b) $\triangledown + \square = I$
   (c) $\odot \times \square = \odot$
   (d) $\odot \times ? = ?$
   (e) $\pi \div \mp = \odot$
   (f) $\square + \square + \square + \square = \odot$
   (g) $\pi - \mp = \triangledown$
   (h) $* \times * = \uparrow$

3. Again the same ten symbols are used but with different values.

   (a) $\triangledown + \odot = \uparrow$
   (b) $\mp - \pi = *$
   (c) $\ominus \times \ominus \times \ominus = \square$
   (d) $* \times \uparrow = \uparrow$
   (e) $\square \div \triangledown = \ominus$
   (f) $\pi - \triangledown = *$
   (g) $? - \uparrow = \ominus$
   (h) $\odot \times \odot = ?$

Crossnumbers

(a) Copy out the crossnumber pattern.
(b) Fit all the given numbers into the correct spaces. Tick off the numbers from the lists as you write them in the square.

1.

2 digits	3 digits	4 digits	5 digits
13	137	2235	17896
17	151	2635	20146
35	427	4135	24319
47	429	4418	36528
49	607	4426	46712
60	753	4496	58722
61		5063	69761
62		6157	79263
		8517	82245
		8826	84625
		9412	84645

6 digits	7 digits
664728	7588052
668128	
685728	

2.

2 digits		3 digits	4 digits	5 digits	6 digits
11	53	111	2905	10752	523416
12	63	134	3072	12282	538222
17	66	499	3141	15216	762214
25	70	525	3333	18253	
28	73	571	4951	25837	
29	74	576	7364	26275	
30	78	611	9362	31785	
32	81	773	9591	43567	
35	82	817		47907	7 digits
38	83			50078	2308712
41	85			69073	4284173
44	91			77527	
47	99			83114	
				95392	

How many dots?: an investigation

1. The diagram shows a 5×5 square of dots.
   There are 16 dots on the perimeter
   and 9 dots inside the square.

   (a) Draw a 3×3, a 4×4 and a 6×6 square of dots. For each diagram, count the number of dots on the perimeter and the number of dots inside the square.

   (b) For a 100×100 square of dots, how many dots are on the perimeter?

   (c) For a 57×57 square of dots, how many dots are inside the square?

2. Rectangles are drawn so that the width is always 1 unit more than the height. The number of dots on the perimeter and the number of dots inside the rectangle are counted.

   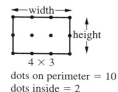

   (a) How many dots are on the perimeter of a 101×100 rectangle?
   (b) How many dots are inside a 9×8 rectangle?
   (c) (Much harder) How many dots are inside a 52×51 rectangle?

Perimeters and common edges: an investigation

In this work, one centimetre squares touch either along an edge or at a corner.

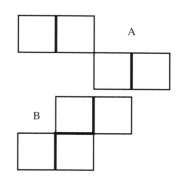

Shape A has two common edges, shown by the thick lines, and shape B has 3 common edges.

The perimeter of shape A is 12 cm and the perimeter of shape B is 10 cm.

- Using four squares, draw a shape with 1 common edge ($c = 1$). Write down the perimeter, p cm.

  Is there more than one shape with one common edge? Do all shapes with one common edge have the same perimeter?

- Again using four squares, draw a shape with 4 common edges ($c = 4$). Write down the perimeter, p, of the shape.

- Draw shapes with $c = 2$, $c = 3$, $c = 0$ and each time write down the perimeter.

- Try to find a connection between c and p. Either write the connection in words or as a formula, '$p = \ldots$'.

Five squares or more

- Draw several shapes with 5 squares with $c = 0, 1, 2 \ldots$
  Find a formula connecting c and p. [Write $p = \ldots$]

- Now draw diagrams with 6 squares and again find a formula connecting c and p.

- Look at your formulas for shapes with 4, 5 and 6 squares. *Predict*, without drawing any more shapes, what the formula might be for 7 squares.

- Now draw several shapes with 7 squares, count c and p for each one, and check if the formula you predicted *does* work.

- Now go further. Predict a formula for shapes with 10 squares, or 100 squares.
  The most *general* case is the shape consisting of n squares, where n is any whole number (greater than 1).
  Try to write a formula connecting c, p and n.

Extension

- Equilateral triangles can be drawn on isometric paper.
  For shape X, $c = 2$ and $p = 8$.
  For shape Y, $c = 1$ and $p = 10$.

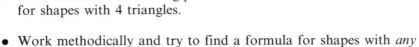

- Find a formula connecting p and c for shapes with 4 triangles.

- Work methodically and try to find a formula for shapes with *any* number of triangles.

Further extension

- *Without* drawing any shapes, try to predict a formula, connecting p and c, for 3 hexagons.

- Draw shapes with 3 hexagons and check if your formula works.

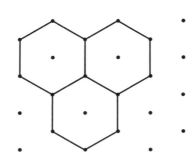

Part 6

6.1 Locus

A locus is the set of points which fit a certain description. Sometimes a locus can be described in words, sometimes it is better to draw a diagram. The plural of locus is loci.

(a) Suppose television reception is 'good' within 100 km of a transmitter T. The diagram shows the locus of points where the reception is 'good'.

Here the locus is the boundary and all the points inside the circle.

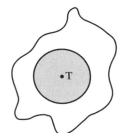

(b) The dotted line shows the locus of a tennis ball which is thrown and then bounces on a tennis court.

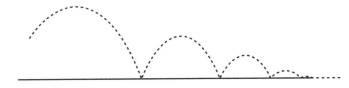

(c) Find the locus of points which are an equal distance from the points A and B. (we say 'equidistant' from A and B).

A•

•B

> This is an important and common locus construction. [See section 2.2]

Take a pair of compasses and set the radius at more than half the length AB. With centre A draw two arcs. With the same radius and centre B draw two more arcs. Draw a straight line through the points where the arcs cut. This is the locus of points equidistant from A and B. (shown with a broken line).

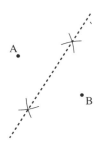

Exercise 1

1. Draw the locus of a point P which moves so that it is always 4 cm from a fixed point A.

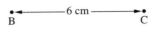

2. Draw points B and C 6 cm apart. Draw the locus of a point P which moves so that it is equidistant from B and C.

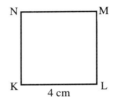

3. Draw the square KLMN. A tiny spider wanders around inside the square so that it is always nearer to corner K than to corner L. Shade the region to show the locus of the spider.

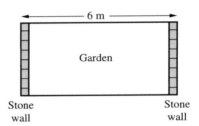

4. A newt crawls across a rectangular garden so that it is always at an equal distance from the two stone walls. Draw a sketch to show the locus of the newt.

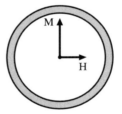

5. (a) Describe in words the locus of M, the tip of the minute hand, as the time changes from 3 o'clock to 4 o'clock.
   (b) Sketch the locus of H, the tip of the hour hand, as the time changes from 3 o'clock to 6 o'clock.

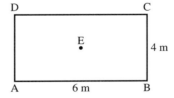

6. The diagram shows a rectangular room ABCD. Draw three diagrams with a scale of 1 cm to 1 m to illustrate the following loci:
   (a) Points in the room up to 3 m from A
   (b) Points in the room up to 2 m from E, the centre of the room.
   (c) Points in the room equidistant from A and B.

7. A snake's cage is built against a wall, as shown. The public are not allowed to be within one metre of the cage.
   Sketch the cage and show the locus of points where the public are not allowed.

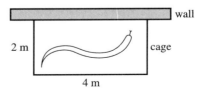

A submarine is known to be within 26 km of port P. The submarine is also known to be within 15 km of port Q. Show the region where the submarine must be.

(a) Draw an arc of radius 2·6 cm with centre P.
(b) Draw an arc of radius 1·5 cm with centre Q.
(c) The submarine must lie inside both arcs so it lies in the shaded region.

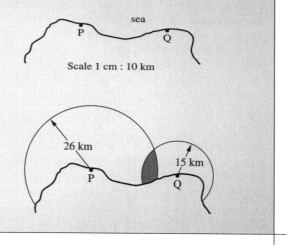

Exercise 2

1. Inspector Clouseau has put a radio transmitter on a suspect's car, which is parked somewhere in Paris. From the strength of the signals received at points R and P, Clouseau knows that the car is
   (a) not more than 40 km from R, and
   (b) not more than 20 km from P.

   Make a scale drawing [1 cm ≡ 10 km] and show the possible positions of the suspect's car.

2. A treasure is buried in the rectangular garden shown. The treasure is:
   (a) within 4 m of A and
   (b) more than 3 m from the line AD.
   Draw a plan of the garden and shade the points where the treasure could be.

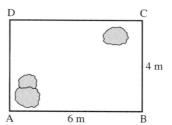

3. Draw four copies of square KLMN and show the locus of points *inside the square* which are:
   (a) within 3 cm of the mid point of KL,
   (b) equidistant from K and M,
   (c) nearer to M than to K,
   (d) more than 5 cm from N.

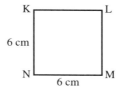

4. A goat is tied to one corner on the outside of a barn.
The diagram shows a plan view.
Sketch a plan view of the barn and show the locus of points where the goat can graze if the rope is 4 m long.

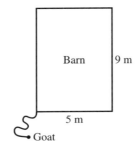

5. Draw a line AB of length 10 cm. With AB as base draw a triangle ABP so that the *area* of the triangle is 30 cm². Describe the locus of P if P moves so that the area of the triangle ABP is always 30 cm².

6. A conker is hanging motionless on a string. I move a finger so that its tip is always 20 cm from the conker. Describe the locus of my finger tip.

7. A rectangular paving slab is rotated 90° about corner A as shown.
(a) Copy the diagram and use a pair of compasses to draw the locus of X during the first rotation.
(b) The slab is then rotated a further 90° clockwise, this time about the corner B. Draw the new position of the slab. Use compasses to draw the path of X during this second rotation.

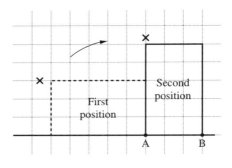

8. Draw two points A and B 10 cm apart.

Place the corner of a piece of paper (or a set square) so that the edges of the paper pass through A and B.
Mark the position of corner C.
Slide the paper around so the edges still passes through A and B and mark the new position of C. Repeat several times and describe the locus of the point C which moves so that angle ACB is always 90°.

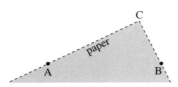

6.2 Probability

Methods of estimating probability

The probability of an event is a measure of the chance of it happening. Probability is measured on a scale from 0 to 1. An event which is impossible has a probability of 0. An event which is certain has a probability of 1.

There are four different ways of estimating probabilities.

Method A
Use symmetry

- The probability of rolling a 3 on a fair dice is $\frac{1}{6}$.
  This is because all the scores 1, 2, 3, 4, 5, 6 are equally likely.
- Similarly the probability of getting a head when tossing a fair coin is $\frac{1}{2}$.

Method B
Conduct an experiment or survey to collect data

- Suppose I wanted to estimate the probability of a drawing pin landing point upwards when dropped onto a hard surface. I could not use symmetry for obvious reasons but I could conduct an experiment to see what happened in, say, 500 trials.

- I might want to know the probability that the next car going past the school gates has only one occupant.
  I could conduct a survey in which the number of people in cars is recorded over a period of time.

Method C
Look at past data

Suppose I wanted to estimate the probability that there will be snow in the ski resort to which a school party is going in February next year. I could look at weather records for the area over the last 10 or 20 years.

Method D
Make a subjective estimate

We have to use this method when the event is not repeatable. It is not really a 'method' in the same sense as are methods A, B, C.

- We might want to estimate the probability of England beating France in a soccer match next week. We could look at past results but these could be of little value for all sorts of reasons. We might consult 'experts' but even they are notoriously inaccurate in their predictions.

Exercise 1

In Questions **1** to **10** state which method A, B, C or D you would use to estimate the probability of event given.

1. The probability of drawing a 'king' from a pack of playing cards.

2. The probability that it will rain every day at the site where the school party is going on a camping holiday next year.

3. The probability that a person selected at random would vote 'Conservative' in a general election tomorrow.

4. The probability that your maths teacher will pick the winning six numbers in the National Lottery next week. [There are 13 983 816 ways of choosing 6 numbers from 1 to 49.]

5. The probability that a letter posted 'first class' at 8.00 a.m. today will arrive at its destination tomorrow.

6. The probability that the England cricket team will win the toss in their next three test matches.

7. The probability that someone in your class will be the parent of twins within the next 20 years.

8. The probability that you will throw a 'double' when you roll a pair of fair dice.

9. The probability of spinning a '10' on a roulette wheel which is suspected of being biased.

10. The probability that sometime this week your mother will ask you to tidy your bedroom (unnecessarily!).

Working out probabilities

For simple events, like throwing a dice or selecting a ball from a bag, symmetry can be used to work out the expected probability of the event occurring.

$$\text{Expected probability} = \frac{\text{the number of ways the event can happen}}{\text{the number of possible outcomes}}$$

When an experiment (like rolling a dice or tossing a coin) is repeated several times, we can calculate the number of times we expect an event to occur. Call the event in which we are interested a 'success'.

Expected number of successes = (probability of a success) × (number of trials)

(a) Seven discs numbered 3, 4, 5, 7, 9, 11, 12 are placed in a bag.
One disc is selected at random.
In this example there are 7 possible outcomes of a trial.
(i) p (selecting a '5') $= \frac{1}{7}$
(ii) p (selecting an odd number) $= \frac{5}{7}$
(iii) p (selecting a '10') $= 0$

(b) A fair dice is rolled 540 times. How many times would you expect to roll a '2'.

p (rolling a 2) $= \frac{1}{6}$
Expected number of 2's $= \frac{1}{6} \times 540$
$= 90$

Some events can either 'happen' or 'not happen'.

Probability of an event not happening = 1 − (Probability of the event happening)

(a) The spinner shown has equal sectors.

(i) p (spinning a 3) $= \frac{1}{8}$
(ii) p (not spinning a 3) $= 1 - \frac{1}{8} = \frac{7}{8}$

(b) The probability of a drawing pin landing 'point up' is 0·61.

Therefore, the probability of the drawing pin landing 'point down' is $1 - 0·61 = 0·39$.

Exercise 2

1. One card is picked at random from a pack of 52.
Find the probability that it is
(a) the Queen of diamonds
(b) a ten
(c) a diamond.

2. Ten discs numbered 1, 3, 3, 3, 4, 7, 8, 9, 11, 11 are placed in a
bag. One disc is selected at random.
Find the probability that it is
(a) an even number
(b) a three
(c) less than 6.

3. David puts these numbered discs in a bag.
(a) He shakes the bag and takes one disc without looking. What
number is he most likely to get?

(b) Erica wants to put discs in a bag so that it is *less likely* that
she will pick a 3 than a 2.
What discs could she put in her bag?

(c) Gary has got these discs in his bag.
He wants to put some more discs in the bag to make it
equally likely that he will pick a 1, a 2 or a 3. What discs
should he add?

David's discs
① ② ② ③
③ ③ ③

Gary's ③
discs
① ①
② ② ②

4. There are 12 balls in a bag. Natasha takes a ball from the bag,
notes its colour and then returns the ball to the bag. She does
this 20 times.
Here are her results.

(a) What is the smallest number of red
balls there *could* be in the bag?

(b) Natasha says 'There cannot be any
yellow balls in the bag because there
are no yellows in my table.'
Explain why Natasha is wrong.

(c) Natasha takes one more ball from
the bag. What is the most likely
colour of the ball?

Red	5
White	1
Green	11
Blue	3

5. A bag contains 9 balls: 3 red, 4 white and 2 yellow.
   (a) Find the probability of selecting a red ball.
   (b) The 2 yellow balls are replaced by 2 white balls. Find the probability of selecting a white ball.

6. Mark played a card game with Paul. The cards were dealt so that both players received two cards. Mark's cards were a five and a four. Paul's first card was a six.

Find the probability that Paul's second card was
(a) a five

(b) a picture card [a King, Queen or Jack].

7. One ball is selected at random from the bag shown and then replaced. This procedure is repeated 400 times. How many times would you expect to select:
   (a) a blue ball,

   (b) a white ball?

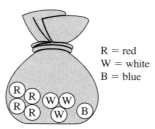

R = red
W = white
B = blue

8. A spinner, with 12 equal sectors, is spun 420 times. How often would you expect to spin:
   (a) an E,

   (b) an even number,

   (c) a vowel?

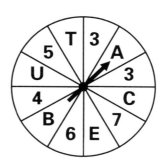

9. Heena puts 4 white balls and 1 black ball in a bag. She then takes out one ball without looking.

(a) Heena asks her parents about the probability of getting a black.

Her mum says,
'It is $\frac{1}{4}$ because there are 4 whites and 1 black.'

Her dad says,
'It is $\frac{1}{5}$ because there are 5 balls and only 1 black.'

Which of her parents is correct?

(b) Carl has another bag containing red and white balls. The probability of picking a red ball from Carl's bag is $\frac{4}{7}$. What is the probability of picking a white ball from Carl's bag?

(c) How many balls of each colour *could* be in Carl's bag?

10. The number of people visiting Tower Bridge one day was 11,249. How many of these people would you expect to celebrate their birthdays on a Tuesday in the year 2010?

11. When playing Monopoly, Philip knows that the probability of throwing a 'double' with two dice is $\frac{1}{6}$. What is the probability that he does *not* throw a double with his next throw?

12. Kevin bought one ticket in a raffle in which 200 tickets were sold. What is the probability that Kevin did not win the first prize?

13. A coin is biased so that the probability of tossing a head is 56%.
(a) What is the probability of tossing a tail with this coin?
(b) How many tails would you expect when the coin is tossed 500 times?

14. One ball is selected from a bag containing x red balls and y blue balls. What is the probability of selecting a red ball?

Listing possible outcomes

When an experiment involves two events, it is usually helpful to make a list of all the possible outcomes. When there is a large number of outcomes, it is important to be systematic in making the list.

- Coins
  Using H for 'head' and T for 'tail', two coins can land as:

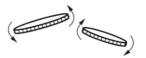

H	H
H	T
T	H
T	T

● Two dice

When a red dice is thrown with a white dice, the outcomes are (red dice first):

(1, 1), (1, 2), (1, 3), (1, 4), (1, 5), (1, 6), (2, 1), (2, 2), (2, 3) ... (6, 6).

The 36 equally likely outcomes can be shown on a grid. Point A shows a 4 on the red dice and a 5 on the white dice. Point B shows a 2 on the red dice and a 4 on the white dice.

The probability of rolling a two on the red dice and a four on the white dice is $\frac{1}{36}$.

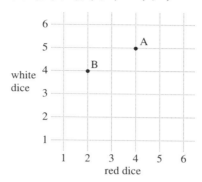

Exercise 3

1. A 10p coin and a 20p coin are tossed together. List all the possible outcomes, heads or tails, for the two coins.

2. Three coins are tossed together. List all the possible outcomes for the three coins.
   What is the probability of tossing three heads?

3. A red dice and a white dice are thrown together.
   (a) Draw a grid to show all the possible outcomes.
   (b) What is the probability of:
       (i) getting the same number on each dice?
       (ii) a total score of 10?
       (iii) the score on the red dice being double the score on the white dice?

4. Katy has these two spinners. She spins both spinners and adds up the numbers to get a total. For example a '10' and a '2' give a total of 12.
   Make a list of all the possible totals.
   What is the probability of getting a total of 8?

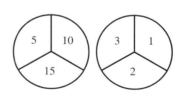

5. A bag contains a 2p coin, a 5p coin and a 10p coin. Two coins are selected at random.
   (a) List all the possible combinations of two coins which can be selected from the bag.
   (b) Find the probability that the total value of the two coins selected is
       (i) 15p
       (ii) 7p
       (iii) 20p

188

6. A coin and a dice are tossed together.
   (a) List all the possible outcomes.
   (b) Find the probability of getting
       (i) a head on the coin and a 6 on the dice
       (ii) a tail on the coin and an even number on the dice.

7. Four friends, Jen, Ken, Len and Mick, each write their name on a card and the four cards are placed in a hat. Two cards are chosen to decide who does the washing-up that day.
   (a) List all the possible combinations.
   (b) What is the probability that Ken and Len are chosen?

8. The spinner is spun and the dice is rolled at the same time.
   (a) Draw a grid to show all the possible outcomes.
   (b) A 'win' occurs when the number on the spinner is greater than the number on the dice.
       Find the probability of a 'win'.

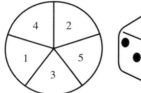

Exclusive events

Events are *mutually exclusive* if they cannot occur at the same time.

Examples

- Selecting a Queen } from a pack
  Selecting a 3   } of cards

- Tossing a 'head'
  Tossing a 'tail'

- Selecting a red ball from a bag
  Selecting a white ball from the same bag.

The sum of the probabilities of mutually exclusive events is 1

Exercise 4

1. A bag contains a large number of balls including some green balls. The probability of selecting a green ball is $\frac{1}{4}$. What is the probability of selecting a ball which is not green?

2. A bag contains balls which are either red, blue or yellow.
   The probability of selecting a red is 0·3
   The probability of selecting a blue is 0·4
   What is the probability of selecting a yellow?

3. A bag contains balls which are either red, white or green.
   The probability of selecting a red ball is 0·1
   The probability of selecting a white ball is 0·6
   (a) Find the probability of selecting a green ball?
   (b) Find the probability of selecting a ball which is not red?

4. In a game using an electronic spinner, four possible symbols can be obtained.
   The probability of each occurring is:

Star prize	$\frac{1}{16}$
Cat	$\frac{1}{8}$
Mouse	$\frac{1}{4}$
Lose	?

   Find the probability of:
   (a) losing
   (b) getting 'cat' or 'mouse'
   (c) not getting 'Star prize'.

5. A bag contains a large number of discs.
   Most are numbered 1, 2, 3 or 4.
   The rest are blank.
   Here are the probabilities of drawing a disc with a particular number:

$p(1) = 0·2$
$p(2) = 0·15$
$p(3) = 0·25$
$p(4) = 0·1$

   What is the probability of drawing a disc,
   (a) marked 1 or 2?
   (b) marked 2, 3 or 4?
   (c) which is blank?

6.3 Gradient, $y = mx + c$

- If we know the coordinates of two points on a line, we can use the formula

$$\text{Gradient} = \frac{\text{Difference between } y \text{ coordinates}}{\text{Difference between } x \text{ coordinates}}$$

The gradient of a line tells us how steep it is.
- Consider the line which passes through (1, 2) and (3, 6).

$$\text{Gradient} = \frac{6-2}{3-1} = \frac{4}{2} = 2$$

Notice that:

- a line sloping upwards to the right has a positive gradient;
- a line sloping downwards to the right has a negative gradient.

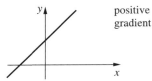 positive gradient

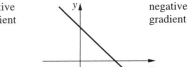 negative gradient

[Some people think of a capital 'N' for negative.]

Exercise 1

1. Find the gradient of the line joining
  (a) (1, 3) and (2, 6)   (b) (1, 3) and (3, 7)
  (c) (2, 5) and (6, 7)   (d) (3, 9) and (9, 11)
  (e) (1, 4) and (3, 2)   (f) (2, 5) and (5, −1)
  (g) (6, 2) and (2, 10)   (h) (3, −2) and (−3, 2)
  (i) (−2, −4) and (−1, 2) (j) (2, −3) and (−2, 6).

2. Find the gradient of the line joining:
  (a) A and B
  (b) B and C
  (c) C and D
  (d) D and A.

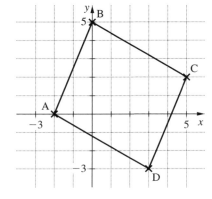

Gradient and intercept

A straight line can be described in terms of

(a) its gradient
(b) where it crosses the y-axis (the y-intercept).

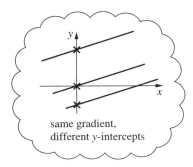

same gradient,
different y-intercepts

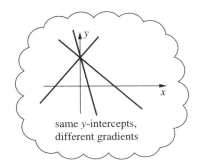

same y-intercepts,
different gradients

Exercise 2

Sketch the following straight lines. Use a new pair of axes for each question. Draw about six sketches on one page of your book.

1. Gradient 2, y-intercept 3.　　**2.** Gradient 1, y-intercept -3.

3. Gradient 2, y-intercept 0.　　**4.** Gradient -1, y-intercept 4.

5. Gradient -3, y-intercept 0.　　**6.** Gradient -2, y-intercept -2.

7. Give the gradient and y-intercept of each line.

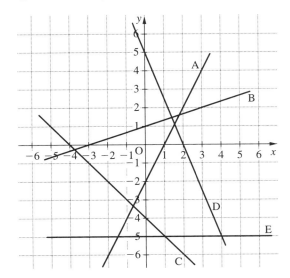

The line $y = mx + c$

$y = mx + c$ is the equation of a straight line with

- gradient m, and
- intercept c. [Hereafter the word 'intercept' is taken to be the y-intercept.]

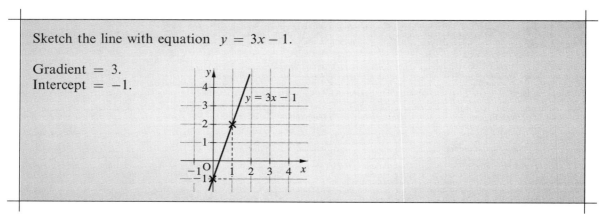

Sketch the line with equation $y = 3x - 1$.

Gradient $= 3$.
Intercept $= -1$.

Exercise 3

Write down the gradient and intercept of each of the following lines:

1. $y = 2x - 3$

2. $y = 3x + 2$

3. $y = -x - 4$

4. $y = \frac{1}{2}x + 3$ Careful!

5. $y = -\frac{2}{3}x - 4$

6. $y = 2 - 3x$

7. $y = 4 - 7x$

8. $y = 2x - 1$

9. $y = 3 - \frac{1}{2}x$

10. $y = 7 - 2x$

In Questions **11** to **16** make y the subject and write down the gradient and intercept of the corresponding line:

11. $2x + y - 6 = 0$

12. $y - 3x + 7 = 0$

13. $y - 2x = 8$

14. $3x + 6y - 10 = 0$

15. $2x - 5y + 12 = 0$

16. $3y - 9x + 2 = 0$

Sketch each of the following lines:

17. $y = x + 2$

18. $y = 2x - 4$

19. $y = 3 - 2x$

20. $y = \frac{3}{4}x - 1$

21. $y = 2 - \frac{1}{3}x$ **22.** $y - 2x + 2 = 0$

23. $2x + 4y + 1 = 0$ **24.** $3y - 9x - 1 = 0$

In Questions **25** to **30** match each sketch with the correct equation from the list below.

25.
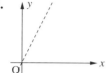

26.

27.
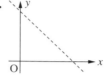

28.
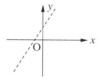

29.
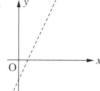

30.

(a) $y = -x - 4$
(d) $y = 3x$

(b) $y = 2x - 1$
(e) $y = 3 - x$

(c) $y = 2x + 3$
(f) $y = 5$

6.4 Number and algebra check-up

Non-calculator arithmetic

Test 1

1. $3 \cdot 2 + 6$ **2.** $2 \cdot 9 \div 10$

3. $2 \cdot 9 \times 10$ **4.** £3 − £1·20

5. £6·50 − £4·20   **6.** $0 \cdot 73 \times 10$

7. $0 \cdot 123 \times 100$ **8.** $444 \div 10$

9. Write 'seventeen pounds 17p' in figures.

10. Write 'seven pounds 7p' in figures.

11. $3 \cdot 2 + 0 \cdot 07$ **12.** $5 - 1 \cdot 6$

13. $14 \cdot 7 - 10$ **14.** $0 \cdot 95 \times 100$

15. $0 \cdot 12 \div 6$ **16.** £8 − £3·65

17. £10 − £7·15   **18.** $1 + 1 \cdot 1 + 2 \cdot 2$

19. $0 \cdot 1 \times 0 \cdot 1$ **20.** $6 \cdot 5 \div 0 \cdot 05$

Test 2

1. $4 \cdot 2 \times 10$ **2.** $0 \cdot 63 \times 10$

3. $5 \cdot 3 + 4$ **4.** $6 \cdot 2 - 5$

5. $4 \cdot 8 \div 4$ **6.** $73 \cdot 6 \div 10$

7. $213 \div 100$ **8.** $8 \cdot 6 \times 10$

9. $0 \cdot 71 \times 10$ **10.** $1 \cdot 3 + 0 \cdot 6$

11. $2 \cdot 7 - 0 \cdot 5$ **12.** $5 \cdot 4 + 5$

13. Write 'five pounds 40p' in figures

14. Write 'five pounds 4p' in figures

15. $550 - 376$ **16.** $0 \cdot 6 \times 100$

17. $3 \cdot 6 \div 0 \cdot 3$ **18.** $0 \cdot 09 \div 9$

19. $1 \cdot 2 + 2 \cdot 17$ **20.** £5 − £2·75

Number check-up

Do not use a calculator

A Index numbers: simplify

1. $3 \times 3 \times 3 \times 3 \times 3$
2. $4^3 \times 4^4$
3. $7^2 \times 7^4$
4. $8^5 \div 8^2$
5. $9^7 \div 9^2$
6. $5^2 \times 5^3 \times 5^4$
7. $11^8 \div 11^2$
8. $(6 \times 6 \times 6)^2$

B Order of operations: work out

1. $4 + 6 \times 2$
2. $8 + 12 \div 2$
3. $3^2 + 4 \times 2$
4. $10 - (7 - 3)$
5. $(12 \times 4) \div 6$
6. $12 - (2^3 + 1)$
7. $15 - 8 \div 2$
8. $11 \times (4^2 - 16)$

C Fractions: work out

1. $\frac{3}{4} \times \frac{1}{5}$
2. $\frac{2}{7} \times \frac{1}{4}$
3. $\frac{1}{2} \div \frac{1}{3}$
4. $\frac{1}{10} \div \frac{2}{5}$
5. $\frac{7}{8} - \frac{1}{2}$
6. $\frac{7}{10} + \frac{1}{5}$
7. $\frac{3}{16} + \frac{1}{4}$
8. $\frac{8}{9} \times \frac{6}{10}$

D Decimals: work out

1. $8 + 1 \cdot 2$
2. $7 - 2 \cdot 4$
3. $11 \times 0 \cdot 2$
4. $22 \times 0 \cdot 04$
5. $1 \cdot 52 \div 0 \cdot 1$
6. $5 \cdot 62 \div 0 \cdot 2$
7. $100 \times 0 \cdot 32$
8. $0 \cdot 1 \div 0 \cdot 2$

E Percentages

1. Increase £25 by 5%
2. Decrease £200 by 7%
3. Find 11% of £60

4. A car was bought for £5000 and sold for £5400. Find the percentage profit.

F Negative numbers

1. $-8 + 11$
2. $-3 - 4$
3. $(-2) \times 5$
4. $4 - (-2)$
5. $(-3) \times (-5)$
6. $8 + (-3)$
7. $7 - 15$
8. $20 \div (-4)$

G Estimation. Estimate the answer

1. $49 \cdot 2 \times 2 \cdot 07$
2. $0 \cdot 971 \times 307 \cdot 4$
3. $6154 \times 19 \cdot 7$
4. $407 \div 19 \cdot 2$

H Miscellaneous

1. Which of the following is/are prime numbers?

$$\boxed{15, \ 17, \ 33, \ 39, \ 41, \ 49}$$

2. List the factors of   (a) 18   (b) 30

3. Write down the first four multiples of   (a) 5   (b) 9

4. How many of these statements are true?

$\frac{2}{5} = 0 \cdot 4$ 5% of $50 = 2 \cdot 5$ $0 \cdot 2 = 20\%$ $0 \cdot 2 \times 0 \cdot 3 = 0 \cdot 6$

5. Copy and complete these magic squares

(a)
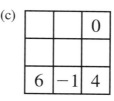

4	3	
	5	
		6

(b)

	−3	2
	1	
	5	

(c)

		0
6	−1	4

Negative numbers

Perform each calculation and write down the corresponding letter from the list below, to make a sentence.

A. $5 - 8$; $-3 - 2$; $(-2)^2$; $3^2 - 20$; $6 \div (-6)$; $(-2)^2 + 3$; $-5 + (-3)$; $(-49) \div (-7)$; $-3 - (-5)$; $(-5) \times (-1)$; $-7 + 11$; $4^2 - 4$; $-1 + 13$; $(-1)^2 \times 4$; $30 \div (-10)$; $-2 + 9$; $(-3\frac{1}{2}) \times 2$; $(-8) \div (-2)$; $(-1) \div \frac{1}{10}$; $8 - 11$; $(-7)^2 + (-1)^2$; $-6 - 5$; $(-10) \times \frac{1}{2}$; $-3 + 10$; $(-2)^3 - 2$; $3 - (-5)$; $(-3) \times (-4)$; $(-16) \div (-2)$; $2 \div (-4)$? $(-6 - 2) \times (-1)$; $2 \times (-5)^2$; $(-6)^2 \div 3$; $(-2) \times (-2) \times 2$; $-5 + 13$; $-12 - (-2)$.

B. $-11 + 8$; $-3 + (-2)$; $(-2)^2$; $1 - 12$; $3 \times (-1)$; $1 - (-6)$; $-2 + 4$; $(-3) \times (-4)$; $6 \div (-6)$; $(-16) \div 2$; $(-3\frac{1}{2}) \times -2$; $2^2 - 2$; $1 \div (\frac{1}{2})$; $-7 - (-7)$; $(-3)^2 - 1$; $-3 - 8$; $(-14) \div (-2)$; $-3 + 8$; $-8 + 15$; $(-1)^2 + (-1)^2$; $(-5) \times 2$; $-1 - 10$; $(-2) \div (-\frac{1}{2})$; $-2 - 2 - 1$; 2^3; $4 + (-6)$; $(-1)^5$; $-3 + 10$; $(-6) \div (-1)$; $2 - (-3)$; $(-3 - 4) \times (-1)$; $19 - 22$; $(-5) \times 0$? $(-2)^3 \div (-2)$; $-2 + 7$; $1 - (-6)$; $3 \times (-1)$; $(-50) \div (-10)$; $0 \cdot 1 \times 20$; $3^2 + 2^2 - 1^2$; $(-1) \div (-\frac{1}{4})$; $(-2)^3 - 3$; $\frac{1}{7} \times 49$; $4^3 - 66$.

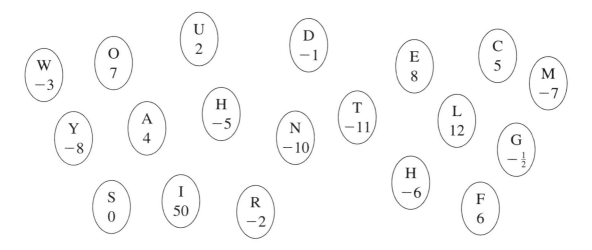

Numeracy test (no calculators)

1. Copy each line and write $+$, $-$, $\times$ or $\div$ in the circle to make the calculation correct

    (a) $12 \times 5 \bigcirc 3 = 180$

    (b) $8 \bigcirc 4 + 5 = 37$

    (c) $84 \bigcirc 7 - 5 = 7$

2. $732 - 257 = ?$

3. $54 \times 32 = ?$

4. $2478 \div 7 = ?$

5. $4131 \div 17 = ?$

6. A paper girl is paid £2·50 for morning deliveries. This is her rate for Monday to Saturday. She is paid time and a half for Sunday deliveries. How much does she earn in a working week?

7. A young man in a supermarket is paid £4 per hour. He is given a 5% increase in pay. What is his new rate of pay per hour?

8. A metal bar 375 mm long has to be machine cut into 5 equal pieces. How long is each piece?

9. What is the reading shown on this scale?

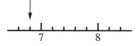

10. Write down any number between 13·2 and 13·3

11. Write down any number between 8·64 and 8·65.

12. How many $\frac{1}{8}$'s are there in $\frac{3}{4}$?

13. A road is 690 cm wide. What is the width of the road in metres?

14. A piece of string is 1500 cm long. How many metres is this?

15. A bag contains 5 kg of dog biscuits. How much is this in grams?

16. If I buy 5 tins of drink each of capacity 2000 ml, how many litres is this altogether?

17. A carpenter needs three pieces of wood of lengths 65 cm, 95 cm and 1·15 m.
What is the total length of wood he needs?

18. What is the perimeter of this rectangle (in metres)?

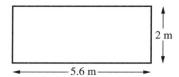

19. A train leaves St Pancras at 15.35 and arrives in Nottingham at 17.10. How long does the journey take?

20. A television programme starts at 18.50 and lasts for 1 hour 45 minutes. At what time does the programme end?

21. What percentage of this rectangle is shaded?

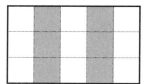

22. Fill in the missing numbers so that the answer is always 27

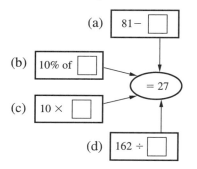

Algebra check-up

1. Solve the equations

(a) $3x - 1 = 1 + 2x$

(b) $4(2x - 1) = 3(x + 2)$

(c) $\dfrac{x - 1}{2} = 5$

(d) $\dfrac{x}{5} + 4 = 10$

2. Find the value of each expression when $x = 3$, $y = -2$, $z = -1$.

(a) $x^2 + y^2$

(b) $xy + 3z$

(c) $2x^2$

(d) $yz - x^2$

(e) $\dfrac{x + y}{z}$

(f) $3y^2 + z^2$

3. Remove the brackets and simplify.

(a) $3(2x - 1) + 2(x + 4)$

(b) $4(x + 3) + 5(2x - 1)$

(c) $2(3a + 5) - 3(a - 1)$

(d) $7(2a - 1) - 5(a + 2)$

4. Simplify

(a) $\dfrac{n + n + n + n}{n}$

(b) $\dfrac{m + m + m}{3}$

(c) $m - n + m - n$

(d) $\dfrac{n}{n}$

(e) $\dfrac{n^2}{n}$

(f) $n^2 \times n$

5. Use trial and improvement to find one solution, correct to one decimal place.

(a) $x(x + 4) = 30$

(b) $x^3 + 3x = 100$

6. Find the value of x so that the areas of the shaded rectangles are equal.

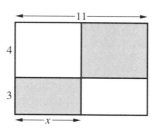

7. The equation of the line could be:

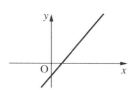

A $y = 2x + 1$
B $y = 3x - 1$
C $y = 4x$
D $y = -3x - 1$

8. Write down what you get if you subtract three from x and then double the result.

A $2x - 3$
B $x^2 - 3$
C $(x - 3)^2$
D $2(x - 3)$

6.5 KS3 Practice papers

The questions in these practice papers are written to reflect the style and content of questions in recent KS3 papers at levels 4–6 and 5–7.

Paper 1. You may use a calculator but remember to show your working.

1. Triangle A was reflected onto triangle B.

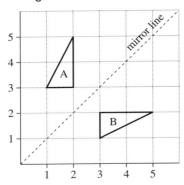

Here are the coordinates of the triangles:

Triangle A	Triangle B
(1, 3)	(3, 1)
(2, 3)	(3, 2)
(2, 5)	(5, 2)

(a) Describe what happens to the co-ordinates of each corner.

(b) Triangle C with co-ordinates (6, 2), (8, 5), (9, 4) is reflected in the same line onto triangle D. Write down the co-ordinates of the corners of triangle D.

2. Carine wants to buy 9 drinks at 29p each but she has only £3 to spend. *Without* using a calculator, show how you can tell that she will have enough money *without* working out the exact answer.

3. Here are four expressions involving an unknown number n

A	B	C	D
$2n + 1$	$n - 5$	$2n + 3$	$3n + 1$

(a) Find the value of n if the expressions A and B are equal.

(b) Find the value of n if the expressions C and D are equal.

(c) Which two expressions could never be equal for *any* value of n?

4. Here are some number cards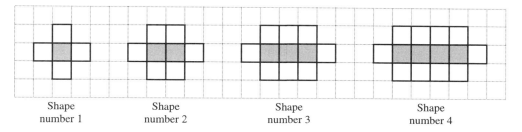

(a) Ian picks the cards | 2 | | 3 | and | 5 | to make the number 235.

What extra card could he take to make a number ten times as big as 325?

(b) Neha chose 3 cards to make the number 4·1
  (i) What cards could she take to make a number ten times as big as 4·1?
  (ii) What cards could she take to make a number 100 times as big as 4·1?

5. This is a series of shapes with black and white tiles.

Shape number 1   Shape number 2   Shape number 3   Shape number 4

(a) How many black tiles and how many white tiles are there in shape number 10?

(b) How many black tiles and how many white tiles are there in shape number 150?

6. Andy, Brian, Chris and Don are in a diving competition. The order in which they dive is decided by drawing cards with their names on from a bag. The names are taken out one at a time without looking.

(a) Write down all the possible orders of diving with Chris going first.

(b) In the main competition there are 12 divers.
The probability that Chris dives first is $\frac{1}{12}$.
Work out the probability that Chris does *not* dive first.

7. Look at these diagrams

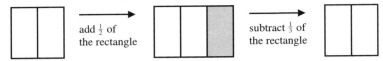

Draw the diagrams below and fill in the missing fractions

(a)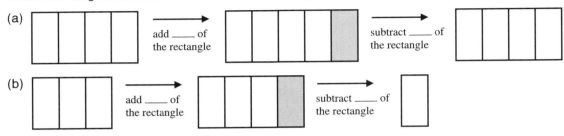

(b)

(c) Draw the missing shapes

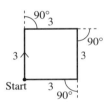

8. The instructions to draw the square are

FORWARD 3, RT 90, FORWARD 3, RT 90,
FORWARD 3, RT 90, FORWARD 3.

Write instructions to draw each of these shapes. For each shape the first instruction is 'FORWARD 4'.

(a) 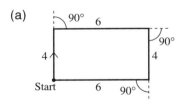   (b)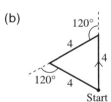

9. A sports shop had a closing down sale.
The sale started on Wednesday.
For each day of the sale, prices were reduced by 20% of the prices on the day before.

A tennis racket had a price of £30 on Tuesday.
What was the price of the racket on Thursday?

10. The diagram shows a flag in the shape of a triangle.
    (a) Find the area of the triangle.

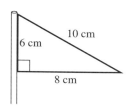

    (b) The flag has a red circle of
        diameter 3 cm. Work out the
        area of this circle.
    (c) A rule for advertising states that
        the area of the circle must be
        less than 30% of the area of the flag.
        Is the area of this circle within the
        rule?

11.

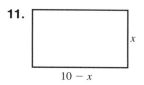

Lisa draws a rectangle with sides x cm
and $(10 - x)$ cm
    (a) Work out the perimeter of the
        rectangle.
    (b) The *area* of the rectangle is 20 cm^2.
        She wants to find x so that
        $x(10 - x) = 20$.

        Between which *one decimal place*
        numbers does x lie?
        Write your answer as 'x is
        between _____ and _____'.

12. Nicola puts 3 white balls and 1 black ball
in a bag. She then takes out one ball
without looking.

    (a) Nicola asks her parents about the
        probability of getting a black ball.
        Her mum says   Her dad says
        'It is $\frac{1}{3}$ because there   'It is $\frac{1}{4}$ because there
        are 3 whites and 1 black.'   are 4 balls and only 1 black.'

        Which of her parents is correct?

    (b) Daniel has another bag containing red and white balls.
        The probability of picking a red ball from the bag is $\frac{3}{8}$.
        What is the probability of picking a white ball from Daniel's
        bag?
    (c) How many balls of each colour *could* be in Daniel's bag?
    (d) Write down another possibility for the number of balls of
        each colour that could be in Daniel's bag.

13. Which of the rectangles A, B, C, D, E, F, G, H are enlargements of rectangle R?

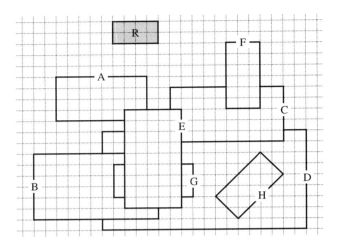

14. A vet does a survey in which he records the number of kittens born in each litter. Here are the results for 20 litters.

Number of kittens	Number of litters
2	1
3	2
4	6
5	5
6	5
7	1

(a) Work out the mean number of kittens born in each litter.

(b) From the table, the mode is 4 and the median is 5.
Every year 400 female cats have kittens.
Work out how many kittens you would expect to be born.
Explain your method.

(c) About how many litters would you expect to have 7 kittens?

15. Chocolates are sold in the boxes shown.
(a) The area of the lid is 165 cm^2.
Work out the volume of the box.

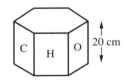

(b)

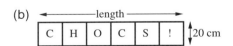

The label that goes round the tin has an area of 960 cm^2.
Work out the distance around the tin.

Paper 2. You may use a calculator but remember to show your working.

1. Copy and complete this shopping bill, filling in the missing amounts

Baking potatoes	1·5 kg at 30p a kg	?
Tomatoes	0·5 kg at 50p a kg	?
Carrots	0·75 kg at 32p a kg	?
Broccoli	0·65 kg at £1·30 a kg	?
Flowers		3.99 +
	Total	?

2. 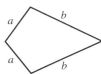 The perimeter of this shape is $2a + 2b$.
We write $p = 2a + 2b$.

Write an expression for the perimeters of each of these shapes.

 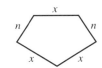 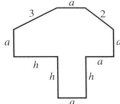

3. Here is information about the sales of snacks. This question is about estimating the total income from sales.
   (a) In your estimate what number will you use instead of 18 973?
   (b) What price will you use for the cost of one snack?
   (c) Work out an estimate for the total income, in pounds, from the sales of the snacks.

> Two sorts of snacks are sold: Twix for 20p and Aero for 40p.
>
> About the same number of Twix and Aero are sold.
>
> Altogether 18 973 snacks were sold.

4. (a) A square tile has sides of length l cm.
   Write an expression for the perimeter of the tile.
   Write the answer as a number multiplied by l.

   (b) A cross is made from five tiles.
   Write an expression for the perimeter of the cross.

   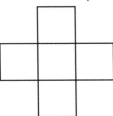

   (c) The perimeter of the cross is 60 cm.
   Use your answer to part (b) to form an equation involving l.
   Solve your equation to find the value of l.

5. Sarita is designing a sticker to go on parcels
Here is a rough sketch of the sticker, which
consists of a semicircle and a triangle.
She needs to know the total height of the
shape.
Make an accurate full size drawing of the
shape and measure its height.

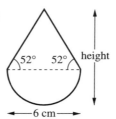

6. Here are some of the ingredients
for a cake using imperial measures.

$\frac{1}{2}$ pound of apples,

1 pint of milk,

2 eggs,

cook the cake in a
12 inch tray.

Copy this table where the amounts
are converted approximately into
metric units.

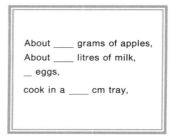

About _____ grams of apples,

About _____ litres of milk,

_ eggs,

cook in a _____ cm tray,

7. The charts show the rainfall recorded in a village over two
months.

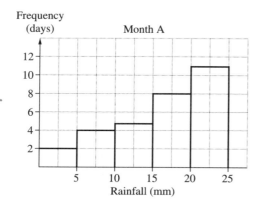

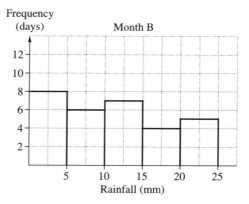

(a) How many days were there in month B?
(b) Katy said 'For month A it rained more at the end of the
month'. Explain whether Katy is right or wrong.
(c) For how many days was there 10 mm or more of rain in
month B?

8. A car dealer sells five makes of car. Here are the records of sales for 1968 and 1998.

Make of car	Sales 1968	Sales 1998
Ford	315	520
Nissan	23	475
Renault	120	240
Rover	655	450
VW	307	311
Total	1420	1996

(a) In 1968 what percentage of the total sales were Ford cars?

(b) In 1968, for every Nissan sold, how many Rovers were sold?

(c) For every Renault sold in 1968, how many were sold in 1998?

(d) Mel thinks that from 1968 to 1998 the sales of VW cars went up by 4%.
Is Mel correct? Explain your answer.

9. Here are 2 spinners.

If I spin the arrow on both of the spinners I could get a 4 followed by a 2 (as shown). I write this as (4, 2).

Write a list of all the combinations of numbers you could get with both spinners, including (4, 2).

10. Houses can be made using matches

  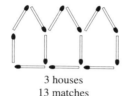

| 1 house | 2 houses | 3 houses |
| 5 matches | 9 matches | 13 matches |

The rule for finding the number of matches is

(multiply the number of houses by 4 and then add 1)

(a) Sam made a pattern with 10 houses. How many matches did he use?

(b) m = number of matches
h = number of houses
Use symbols to write down the rule connecting m and h.

(c) Jack makes a pattern using 37 matches.
How many houses did he make?

11. (a) What is the probability of getting a 6 with this spinner?

(b) Draw a spinner like this with 8 equal sectors. Shade some sectors so that the chance of getting a shaded sector is three times the chance of getting a white sector.

(c) This spinner has some 1s, 2s and 3s written in the sectors. The chance of getting a 2 is twice the chance of getting a 3. The chance of getting a 1 is three times the chance of getting a 3.

Draw the spinner and replace the question marks with the correct number of 1s, 2s and 3s.

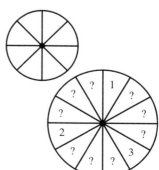

12. (a) Iglis did a survey in which he counted the number of hours for which the television was watched by his family. He kept records for 48 hours of viewing.

Copy the pie chart shown and add sectors to show that 8 hours were spent watching news and 4 hours were spent watching sports.

(b) Joanna conducted a similar survey in her home but she did the survey over 36 hours.
Joanna recorded 12 hours of comedy and $4\frac{1}{2}$ hours of news.
For how many hours were the programmes
   (i)   sports
   (ii) films?

13. Max and Sophie have bikes with different size wheels.
   (a) The wheels on Max's bike have a diameter of 55 cm. Max rolls the bike forward so that the wheels turn round exactly once.
   How far has Max moved?

   (b) The wheels on Sophie's bike have a diameter of 62 cm. Sophie rolls forward a distance of 1200 cm.
   Calculate how many times the wheels go around *completely*.

14. You have to find the answer to this calculation:
$$\frac{53 \times 16 - 18^2}{22 \times 8}$$
Show which keys you press on a calculator.

15. Mr Davis is buying things for his new shop. He buys computers, televisions, videos and phones.
He buys *n* computers.
Your answers to the following questions will involve *n*.

   (a) He buys twice as many televisions as computers. How many televisions does he buy?

   (b) He buys ten more videos than televisions. How many videos does he buy?

   (c) He buys twice as many phones as televisions. How many phones does he buy?

   (d) How many things does he buy altogether?

Paper 3. No calculators allowed.

1. Here is a number machine

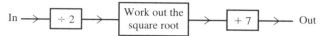

Fill in the spaces to find the numbers which come out.

(a)   8 $\xrightarrow{\div 2}$ 4 $\xrightarrow{\sqrt{}}$ □ $\xrightarrow{+7}$ □

(b)   50 $\longrightarrow$ □ $\longrightarrow$ □ $\longrightarrow$ □

(c) 288 $\longrightarrow$ □ $\longrightarrow$ □ $\longrightarrow$ □

2. Emma's photo measures 4 cm × 6 cm.

(a) She wants to enlarge the photo so that it just fits a frame 12 cm × 18 cm.
   By what scale factor should she multiply the original photo?

(b) Emma also wants a small photo to stick into an identity card.
   The small photo is 2·4 cm by 3·6 cm.
   By what scale factor should she multiply the original photo?

6 cm

4 cm

3. David has four packets of sweets and 5 sweets left over.
Each packet contains n sweets

(a) Which of these expressions gives the correct total number of sweets?

   A $9n$ **B** $(4 + 5)n$ **C** $4n + 5$

(b) There are 73 sweets altogether.
   Form an equation involving n and solve it to find the number of sweets in one packet.

4. The first diagram shows a rectangular block. The second diagram shows the new position after the block is rotated about the corner A.

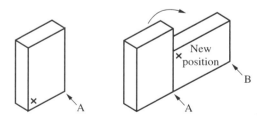

On isometric paper draw the position of the block after it is rotated again, this time about corner B. Draw the X on the diagram.

5. This is shape A. By adding one more square the new shape has the dashed line as a line of symmetry

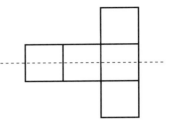

Copy each of the diagrams below and add the number of squares stated so that the dashed line is a line of symmetry.

(a)

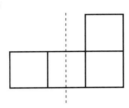

add 1 square

(b)

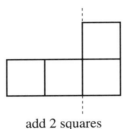

add 2 squares

(c)

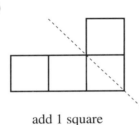

add 1 square

(d)

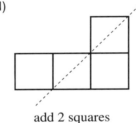

add 2 squares

6. (a) A lorry is loaded with 240 parcels each weighing 37 kg.
Work out the total weight of the parcels.
(b) The maximum load allowed on the lorry is 9 tonnes.
How many more parcels could go on the lorry?
(c) All the parcels have a height of 22 cm.
The height inside the lorry is 190 m.
How many layers of parcels can be put into the lorry?

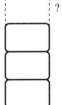

7. The square shown has four lines of symmetry. One line of symmetry is shown by the broken line.
(a) Copy and complete this sentence with the correct equation.
'The broken line has equation
[, $y = -x$; $x + y = 6$; $y = x + 6$].
(b) Write down the equation for each of the other lines of symmetry.

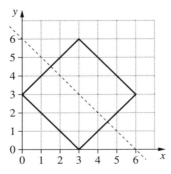

8. Here is a number chain 5 → 8 → 11 → 14 → 17 →
The rule is 'add on 3 each time'.

Here is the start of another number chain 1 → 6 →
(a) Show *three* different ways to continue this number chain

(b) For each chain write down the *rule* you are using.

9. (a) Mel puts a 2 digit whole number
into her calculator. She multiplies
the number by 10.

Fill in *one* other digit which you know must now be on the
calculator.

(b) Mel starts again with the same
2 digit number and this time
she multiplies it by 1000.
Fill in all five digits on the
calculator this time.

10. This solid cube is made from
alternate black and white centimetre cubes.
(a) Find the volume of the black cubes.

(b) How many centimetre cubes are on
the outside of the cube?

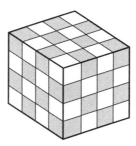

11. The prices for coating a
metal plate with
preservative are:

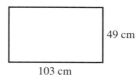

Up to 2000 cm²	£3
From 2000 cm² to 4000 cm²	£5·50
From 4000 cm² to 8000 cm²	£8·50.

The measurements of a plate are shown.
(a) *Estimate* its area. Show your working.

(b) Using your estimate, what price
would you pay for the coating?

(c) Without a calculator, work out the
exact area of the plate.

49 cm

103 cm

6.6 Mathematical games and crossnumbers

Creating numbers: a task requiring imagination

Your task is to create every number from 1 to 50.

You can use only the numbers 1, 2, 3 and 4 once each and the operations $+, -, \times, \div$.

You can use the numbers as powers and you must use *all* of the numbers 1, 2, 3, 4.

Here are some examples:

$$1 = (4 - 3) \div (2 - 1)$$
$$20 = 4^2 + 3 + 1$$
$$68 = 34 \times 2 \times 1$$
$$75 = (4 + 1)^2 \times 3$$

Playing the market

Shares in companies can be bought and sold on the stock market. A company's share price can change considerably over a few months or even days. If, for example, you bought 1000 shares in 'Tottenham' [the soccer club in 'Leisure and Hotels'] at 75p each and then sold them at 167p, you would make a large profit.

Opposite is a selection of companies with their share price in pence. Also shown is the high and low price during the present year and the price change over the previous day.

You have £10 000 to invest and you must spread this over at least 5 companies.

Decide how many shares you wish to buy in each company.

High	Low	Stock	Price	Chg
WATER				
607	442	Anglian	530	x–5
611	454	North West	532	x–11
751	508	Nthumbrian	663	x–1
645	457	Severn Trnt	545	x–2
1740	1525	South Staffs	1740	—
675	484	South West	528	–5
682	466	Southern	582	x–1
611	434$\frac{1}{2}$	Thames	504	–6
744	546	Welsh	646	x–15
759$\frac{1}{2}$	551	Wessex	606	x–2
630	458	Yorkshire	524	x–7

High	Low	Stock	Price	Chg
TELECOMMUNICATIONS				
486	353$\frac{1}{2}$	BT	374$\frac{1}{2}$	–5$\frac{1}{2}$
543	394	Cable & Ws	404	–1$\frac{1}{2}$
1543	1146	Securicor	1463	x–12
1069	785	SecuricorA	950	x–17
892	606	Security Serv	769	x–10
212	157$\frac{1}{2}$	Vodaphone	183$\frac{1}{2}$	—

High	Low	Stock	Price	Chg
RETAILERS, FOOD				
315$\frac{1}{2}$	222$\frac{1}{2}$	Argyll	294$\frac{1}{2}$	–2
68	50$\frac{1}{2}$	Asda	67	x–
505	416	Brake Bros	418	+1
43	24	Budgens	29	x–
656	523	Kwik Save	602	–2
376	138	Low (Willm)	368	–1
480	342	Sainsbury	427	–9
243	30	Shroprite	42	x–
255	200$\frac{1}{2}$	Tesco	248	–3
198	162	Thorntons	193	—
422	279	Watson & P	376	—

High	Low	Stock	Price	Chg
RETAILERS, GENERAL				
80	25	Alexon	28	—
248	203	Allders	217	—
410	330	Argos	330	–5
237	191	Arnotts	231	x–
102	54$\frac{1}{2}$	Ashley (L)	67	+1
357	183	Asprey	183	—
243	176	Austin Reed	242	+1
168	139	Beattie(J)	140	x–1
40	29	Benchmark	29	—
150	110	Bentalls	129	—
165	46	Betterware	46	–4
48	36	Blacks Leis	40	x–
264	198	Body Shop	198	–1
601	504	Boots	520	–2
263	210	Brown (N)	262	—
12$\frac{1}{2}$	2$\frac{3}{4}$	Brown&Jack	3$\frac{1}{4}$	—
74$\frac{1}{2}$	51	Burton	59$\frac{1}{2}$	–1
245	180	Cantors	192	—
304	223	Carpetright	223	–9
246	152	Christies	170	x–1
520	388	Church & Co	501	x–
171	96	Clinton Cds	102	—
258	188	Coles Myer	191	+1
120	24	Colorvision	35	—
903	740	Courts	763	x–9
265$\frac{1}{2}$	5	Dares Ests	10	—

High	Low	Stock	Price	Chg
LEISURE & HOTELS				
40	26	Aberdn Steak	40	—
578$\frac{1}{2}$	417	Airtours	436	–3
46$\frac{1}{2}$	19	Allied Leis	23	—
374	305	Compass	329	–3
25	15	Courtyard	19	—
256	209	David Lloyd	252	–2
213	92	Euro Disney	104	–1
4	2$\frac{1}{2}$	Euro Leisr	3$\frac{1}{2}$	—
290	232	Eurocamp	270	—
455	308	Fairline Bt	455	—
8$\frac{1}{2}$	6	Farringford	6	—
350	262	First Leisr	266	x–
285	209$\frac{1}{2}$	Forte	213	–6
207	169	Friendly Htl	187	—
598	475	Granada	483	x–5
11$\frac{1}{2}$	8	Harmony Leis	8	—
96	62	Hi-Tec Sprt	79	–1
171$\frac{1}{2}$	142$\frac{1}{2}$	Jurys Hotel	167$\frac{3}{4}$	–3$\frac{3}{4}$
18$\frac{1}{4}$	11$\frac{3}{4}$	Lunick	15$\frac{1}{4}$	—
217$\frac{1}{2}$	153	Ladbroke	158$\frac{1}{2}$	x–0$\frac{1}{2}$
263	200	London Clubs	254	–3
104	70	Magnolia	73	–1
702	539	Man Utd	684	—
17	10	Tomorrows	14	–0$\frac{1}{2}$
167	75	Tottenham	133	–2
149	112	Vardon	125	–1
18	7$\frac{1}{2}$	Wembley	8	—
134	110	Zetters	134	x+5

[Ignore the x's.]

When you have finished,
your teacher will give you a
sheet with all the latest prices
(the prices you have above
are 'six months old').

Who has made the largest profit
and who has made the biggest loss?

Teacher's note: See Answer Book
for details of new prices.

'Make your Million' board game

Rules: You are given £10 at the start of the game. The object is to
earn as much money as possible by substituting your dice score
into the expression on your new square. The person with the
biggest balance *when landing on the finish square* wins.

Example. Throwing a 5, then a 1.

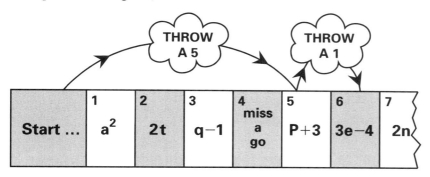

Score on dice	Expression on square	Value of expression using dice score	Balance £
—	—	—	10
5	$P + 3$	$5 + 3 = 8$	$10 + 8 = 18$
1	$3e - 4$	$(3 \times 1) - 4 = 3 - 4 = -1$	$18 - 1 = 17$
•	•	•	•
•	•	•	•

Note:
(i) Landing on 'miss a go' means that your balance remains the
same.
(ii) Landing on 'back to start' means that your balance becomes
zero.

BOARD FOR 'MAKE YOUR MILLION'

START ...	1 a^2	2 2t	3 q−1	4 MISS A GO	5 p+3	6 3e−4	7 2m +3
							8 3r
17 2e+5	16 n^4	15 3(b−2)	14 c^3	13 MISS A GO	12 BACK TO START	11 q−4	10 f^2−9	9 3n−1
18 2m+1							
19 q−3	20 f^2−16	21 3n−5	22 BACK TO START	23 p+2	24 a^2	25 2t	26 MISS A GO	27 6−d
							28 3r
37 8−d	36 f^2−4	35 p+5	34 6e−20	33 3n−4	32 x^5	31 2(b−3)	30 2m+4	29 2−d
38 MISS A GO							
39 a^2	40 3(b−1)	41 2t	42 f^2−9	43 MISS A GO	44 p+1	45 6c	46 5e+4	47 2m+1
							48 4−3e
57 p+6	56 3r	55 q−5	54 BACK TO START	53 10^x	52 a^2	51 MISS A GO	50 10−d	49 5(b−4)
58 12−2d							
59 MISS A GO	60 10^n	61 q−1	62 p+4	63 2m+3	64 2t	65 BACK TO START	... FINISH

Cross numbers

Make three copies of the pattern below and complete the puzzles using the clues given. To avoid confusion it is better not to write the small reference numbers 1, 2... 18 on your patterns. Write any decimal points on the lines between squares.

Part A

Across
1. 15% of 23
2. Next prime number after 23
4. One-third of 2409
5. Solve the equation $\dfrac{x}{5} = 3 \cdot 8$
6. Area of a circle of diameter 30 cm (to nearest whole number)
7. 11×466
9. $245^2 - (3^3 \times 2^2)$
13. $7 + 7^2 + 7^3$
15. $\frac{1}{4} + 3 \times 13$
17. Last 3 digits of (567×7)
18. 50 m written in cm
19. $75 \div 6$

Down
1. Volume of a cube of side 15 cm
2. One minute to midnight on the 24 hour clock
3. $\dfrac{5 \cdot 2}{0 \cdot 21} + \dfrac{17}{0 \cdot 31}$ to 1 d.p.
5. $(11\frac{1}{4})^2$ to the nearest whole number
8. $12 - \frac{1}{100}$
10. Prime number
11. $2^5 - 3$
12. $\frac{3}{7}$ of 3675
13. North-west as a bearing
14. $\frac{3}{4}$ of 11% of 12 000
16. Number of minutes between 1313 and 1745.

Check: There should be 5 decimal points in the puzzle.

Part B

Across	**Down**

Across
1. $(0·5 \div \frac{1}{2}) \times 123$
2. $1001 \div 77$
4. $200 - (4 \div 0·5)$
5. $(2^3 - 1)^2$
6. $33\frac{1}{3}\%$ of 2802
7. $8·14 - (1·96 \times 0·011)$ to 3 d.p.
9. 7391×11
13. $1^1 + 2^2 + 3^3 + 4^4$
15. $10^4 - [2 \times 20^2 + 9 \times 7]$
17. Number of minutes between 0340 and 1310.
18. $80^2 + 9^2 + 1^2$
19. 5% of 388

Down
1. (1 across) × (2 across)
2. $\frac{1}{2} + \frac{1}{3} + \frac{1}{4} + \frac{1}{5}$ to 3 d.p.
3. $20^2 - \sqrt{4}$
5. $42·4 - (8·1 \times 0·13)$ to 1 d.p.
8. 143×7
10. Inches in a foot.
11. $(2^3 \times 3^2) + 2^2 + 2$
12. Number of hours in a leap year.
13. 13% of £22·80, to the nearest penny
14. Next in the sequence
0·858, 8·58, 85·8, ...
16. $113 \times 0·3$

Check: There should be 6 decimal points in the puzzle.

PART C

Across
1. South-west as a bearing.
2. Inches in a yard
4. Last three digits of $(11^2 + 2^2)^2$
5. 4 score plus ten
6. $(26\frac{1}{2})^2$, to the nearest whole number
7. $\frac{24·3}{1·9} + \frac{357}{24} + \frac{87·04}{3·7}$, correct to 2 d.p.
9. $(13 \text{ across})^2 + (5 \text{ across})^2 + 103$
13. $800 - 694$
15. $(550 - 3) \times 11$
17. $4 - 0·95$
18. $\frac{392·2}{(4·97 + 2·66)}$, correct to 2 d.p.
19. Next in the sequence
3, 5, 9, 17, 33, 65

Down
1. A quarter of 1110.
2. 11% of £323·11, to the nearest penny
3. $\frac{1·23}{1·4 - 0·271}$, correct to 2 d.p.
5. $30 \times 31 - 11$
8. Area, in cm^2, of a rectangle measuring 1·2 m by 11 cm
10. (A square number) − 1
11. 80% of 50
12. $\sqrt{(4 \text{ across})} \times (13 \text{ across}) + (10 \text{ down})$
13. Angle in degrees between the hands of a clock at 2·30
14. A quarter share of a third share of a half share of £152·16
16. $76·8 \div 0·4$

Check: There should be 7 decimal points in the puzzle.

Part 7

7.1 Pythagoras' theorem

Below are two dissections which demonstrate a result called Pythagoras' theorem. Pythagoras was a famous Greek mathematician who proved the result in about 550 B.C. The first dissection works only for isosceles right angled triangles.

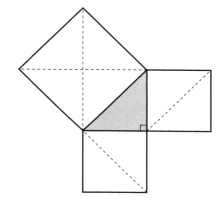

The second dissection, which is Perigal's dissection, is more impressive. It has been left for you to complete as a demonstration of Pythagoras' Theorem.

- Copy triangle ABC on dotted paper.
- Find the point X which is the centre of square ①
- Draw PQ parallel to AB and draw RS perpendicular to PQ.
- Cut out square ② and the four pieces of square ①.
- Rearrange these five pieces to fit exactly into square ③

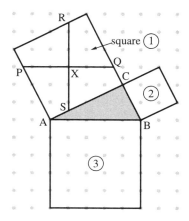

Both of these dissections demonstrate Pythagoras' theorem ....

> 'In a right angled triangle, the square on the hypotenuse is equal to sum of the squares on the other two sides.'

The 'hypotenuse' is the longest side in a right angled triangle.

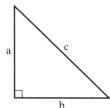

$$a^2 + b^2 = c^2$$

The theorem can be used to calculate the third side of a right angled triangle when two sides are known.

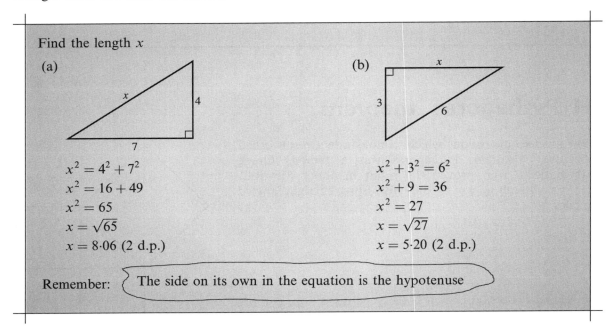

Find the length x

(a)

$x^2 = 4^2 + 7^2$
$x^2 = 16 + 49$
$x^2 = 65$
$x = \sqrt{65}$
$x = 8{\cdot}06$ (2 d.p.)

(b)

$x^2 + 3^2 = 6^2$
$x^2 + 9 = 36$
$x^2 = 27$
$x = \sqrt{27}$
$x = 5{\cdot}20$ (2 d.p.)

Remember: The side on its own in the equation is the hypotenuse

Exercise 1

Give your answers correct to 2 d.p. where necessary. The units are cm unless you are told otherwise.

1. Find x.

(a)   (b)   (c)   (d)

(e)   (f)   (g)   (h)

2. Find y.
Hint: In part (a) write $y^2 + 4^2 = 8^2$

(a)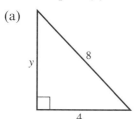

(b)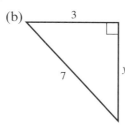

(c)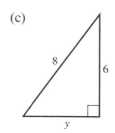

(d)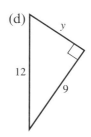

(e)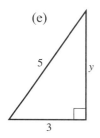

(f)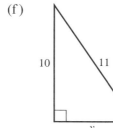

(g)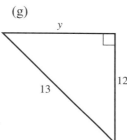

(h)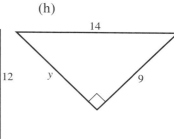

3. Find the side marked with a letter. It may be the hypotenuse or one of the other sides.

(a)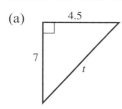

(b)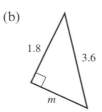

(c)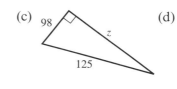

(d)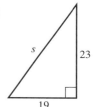

(e)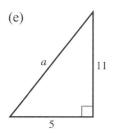

(f)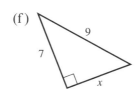

(g)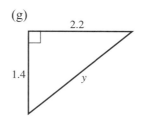

(h)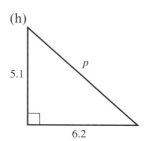

4. A ladder of length 5 m rests against a vertical wall, with its foot 2 m from the wall. How far up the wall does the ladder reach?

5. A ladder of length 4 m reaches 3·2 m up a vertical wall. How far is the foot of the ladder from the wall?

6. The square and the rectangle have the same perimeter. Which has the longer diagonal and by how much?

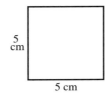
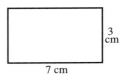

7. A ship sails 40 km due south and then a further 65 km due east. How far is the ship from its starting point?

8. A square has diagonals of length 24 cm. Find the length of a side of the square to the nearest cm.

9. What is the longest shot you could have to play on a snooker table measuring 12 feet by 6 feet?

10. Calculate the height of the isosceles triangle shown.

11. Calculate the vertical height and hence the area of an equilateral triangle of side 14 cm.

12. [More difficult] Find the length x

(a)

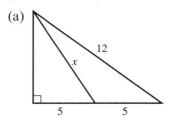

(b)

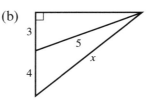

(c)

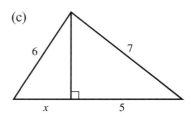

(d)

(e)

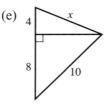

(f)

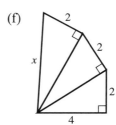

7.2 Compound measures

Speed

When a windsurfer moves at a constant speed of 30 metres per second, it means that he moves a distance of 30 metres in 1 second. In 2 seconds he moves 60 metres. In 3 seconds he moves 90 metres and so on. We see that the distance moved is equal to the speed multiplied by the time taken.

Remember: $\boxed{\text{distance} = \text{speed} \times \text{time}}$ ...①

We obtain two other formulas from ①:

Divide both sides by time: $\boxed{\dfrac{\text{distance}}{\text{time}} = \text{speed}}$ ...②

Divide both sides by speed: $\boxed{\dfrac{\text{distance}}{\text{speed}} = \text{time}}$ ...③

These three important formulas can be remembered using a triangle as shown. [D is at the top]

To find S: cover S, and you have $\dfrac{D}{T}$

To find T: cover T, and you have $\dfrac{D}{S}$

To find D: cover D, and you have $S \times T$

Note: The above formulas can only be used for objects moving at a constant speed.

The units used for speed, distance and time in a question must be compatible.

- If the speed is in miles per hour, the distance must be in miles and the time must be in hours.
- If the speed is in metres per second, the distance must be in metres and the time must be in seconds.

(a) A car is travelling at a steady speed of 25 m/s.

   (i) How far does the car travel in 3·2 s?

   (ii) How long does it take to travel a distance of 11 m?

   (i) distance travelled = speed × time
$$= 25 \times 3{\cdot}2$$
$$= 80 \text{ m}$$

   (ii) time taken $= \dfrac{\text{distance}}{\text{speed}}$
$$= \tfrac{11}{25} = 0{\cdot}44 \text{ s}$$

(b) A bird flies at a speed of 8 m/s for 10 minutes. How far does it fly?

Change 10 minutes into 600 seconds.

distance = speed × time
$$= 8 \times 600$$

The bird flies 4800 m.

Exercise 1

1. A tram travels a distance of 200 m at a speed of 25 m/s. How long does it take?

2. A man runs at a speed of 7·5 m/s. How far will he run in 4 seconds?

3. An arctic tern flies a distance of 245 km in 9 hours. How fast does it fly?

4. A steamroller takes 180 seconds to travel 60 m. What is its speed, in m/s?

5. How long does it take a train to travel 270 km at a constant speed of 90 km/h?

6. A partridge flies 3 miles in 15 minutes. What is its speed in m.p.h.?

7. An aircraft flies at a speed of 940 km/h.
How far does it fly in $2\frac{1}{2}$ hours?

8. If a train travels 60 km in 20 minutes, how far does it go in one hour at the same speed?

9. A horse runs for $1\frac{1}{2}$ hours at a speed of 8 m.p.h. How far does it run?

10. A cyclist takes 30 minutes to travel 11 miles. At what speed does he cycle in m.p.h.?

11. Eurostar goes 420 km from London to Paris in just 3 hours. Find the average speed of the train.

12. Find the distance travelled:
    (a) 65 m.p.h for 2 hours
    (b) 8 cm/day for 5 days
    (c) 5 m/s for 1 minute [units!]

13. A car takes 15 minutes to travel 20 miles. Find the speed in m.p.h.

14. A greyhound runs for 20 s at a speed of 22 m/s. How far does it run?

15. In the 1996 Olympics Donovan Bailey won the 100 m in 9·81 seconds and Michael Johnson won the 200 m in 19·37 seconds. Who ran at the faster average speed?

16. Find the time taken:
    (a) 260 km at 20 km/h
    (b) 2 km at 10 m/s
    (c) 4 miles at 8 m.p.h.

17. A T.G.V. travels 567 km from Bordeaux to Paris at an average speed of 252 km/h. Find the arrival time in Paris, if it leaves Bordeaux at 1410.

18. A boat sails at a speed of 13 knots for 2 days. How far does it travel? [1 knot = 1 nautical mile per hour].

19. In a grand prix, the winning car passed the chequered flag 0·3 seconds ahead of the next car. Both cars were travelling at 84 m/s. What was the distance between the two cars?

Other compound measures

Exercise 2

In Questions **1**, **2**, **3** use the formulas shown.

$$\text{Density} = \frac{\text{Mass}}{\text{Volume}}$$ or $$\text{Mass} = \text{Density} \times \text{Volume}$$

1. Find the density of a metal if $100\,\text{cm}^3$ weighs 800 grams.

2. The density of copper is $9\,\text{g/cm}^3$. Find the mass of a copper bar of volume $20\,\text{cm}^3$.

3. A silver ring has a volume of $3\,\text{cm}^3$ and a mass of 36 grams. Find the density of the silver.

Questions **4** to **9** involve a variety of compound measures.

4. Heavy duty cable costs £1·50 per m. Find the cost of laying 3000 m of this cable.

5. A powerful mainframe computer can be hired at £55 per second. How much will it cost to hire the computer for 1 hour?

6. Gold plating costs £6 per cm^2. How much will it cost to plate this lid?

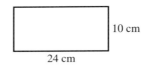

10 cm

24 cm

7. A gambler lost $3·2 million in one year. On average how much did the gambler lose per day? Give your answer to the nearest thousand dollars.

8. Good farmland is sold at £4000 per hectare (1 hectare $= 10\,000\,\text{m}^2$). Bacon farm has a rectangular field measuring 300 m by 80 m. Find the cost of the field.

9. The open box shown is made from metal weighing $5\,\text{g/cm}^2$. Find the weight of the box.

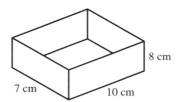

8 cm

7 cm   10 cm

7.3 Inequalities

$x < y$ means 'x is less than y' [or 'y is greater than x']

$p \leqslant q$ means 'p is less than or equal to q' [or 'q is greater than or equal to p'].

$a > b$ means 'a is greater than b' [or 'b is less than a']

$n \geqslant t$ means 'n is greater than or equal to t'.

Notice that the inequality signs can be read from left to right or from right to left.

Illustrate on a number line the range of values of x for which the following inequalities are true:

(a) $x > 1$ — The circle at the left hand end of the range is open. This means that 1 is not included.

(b) $x \leqslant -2$ — The circle at −2 is filled in to indicate that −2 is included.

(c) $-1 \leqslant x < 3$

[−1 included]   [3 not included]

Exercise 1

1. Write down the inequalities displayed. Use x for the variable.

(a)    (b)    (c)

(d)    (e)    (f)

(g)    (h)    (i)

(j)    (k)    (l)

2. Draw a number line to display the following inequalities.

(a) $x > -1$ (b) $x \leqslant 4$ (c) $a > -2$

(d) $n \leqslant 0$ (e) $-5 < p < 5$ (f) $-1 \leqslant y$

(g) $0 \leqslant x \leqslant 10$ (h) $-2 < t \leqslant 7$ (i) $-3 \leqslant s < -1$

3. Answer true or false:

(a) $7 \cdot 1 > 7 \cdot 01$ (b) $-3 < 1$ (c) $3\frac{1}{2} < 3 \cdot 25$ (d) $-6 < -10$

(e) 1 metre > 1 yard   (f) $1 \, \text{kg} > 1$ pound   (g) 1 inch $< 2 \, \text{cm}$ (h) $2^3 < 3^2$

4. If $\square > 520$, write a possible number for $\square$.

5. If $\square < 6400$, write a possible number for $\square$.

6. Write a possible number for $\square$ in each of the following:

(a) $\square < 2450$ (b) $650 < \square$ (c) $200 < \square$

(d) $1500 > \square$ (e) $25\,000 < \square$ (f) $\square > 265$

7. Write a possible number for $\square$ in each of the following:

(a) $1000 < \square < 2000$ (b) $2540 < \square < 2550$ (c) $-3 < \square < 2$

(d) $-5 < \square < -2$ (e) $16\,436 < \square \, 16\,438$ (f) $9842 < \square < 9843$

Solving inequalities

When we solve an equation, like $3x - 1 = x + 9$, we find one value of x which satisfies the equation.

When we solve an inequality, like $2x + 3 < 10$, we find the *range of values* of x which satisfy the inequality.

For example, the solution of the inequality $x - 3 < 11$ is $x < 14$. The variable x can be any value less than 14.

When solving inequalities we can:

- Add the same thing to both sides.

- Subtract the same thing from both sides.

- Multiply or divide both sides by the same *positive* number.

It is better to avoid multiplying or dividing by a *negative* number because then the inequality sign must be *reversed.*

225

Solve the inequalities.

(a) $x - 3 < 4$

Add 3 to both sides.

$x < 7$

(b) $x + 5 > -2$

Subtract 5 from both sides.

$x > -2 - 5$

$x > -7$

(c) $5x \geqslant 350$

Divide both sides by 5.

$x \geqslant 70$

(d) $\dfrac{x}{3} \leqslant -2$

Multiply both sides by 3.

$x \leqslant -6$

Exercise 2

Solve the inequalities.

1. $x - 10 \geqslant 2$ **2.** $x + 6 < 11$ **3.** $y - 6 > -3$

4. $7 + y < 11$ **5.** $3 + x \geqslant 9$ **6.** $x + 1 < 0$

7. $3n \geqslant 48$ **8.** $5y < 1$ **9.** $10x < 1000$

10. $x - 3 < -2$ **11.** $y + 7 > -7$ **12.** $5 + n \geqslant 4$

Find the range of values of x which satisfy each of the following inequalities and show the answer on a number line.

13. $\dfrac{x}{2} < 3$ **14.** $\dfrac{x}{5} > \dfrac{1}{2}$ **15.** $\dfrac{x}{3} \leqslant -1$

16. $-12 \geqslant 3x$ **17.** $\dfrac{1}{4} > \dfrac{x}{2}$ **18.** $\dfrac{3x}{2} > 6$

19. $x - 4 > 0$ **20.** $7 < x + 10$ **21.** $8 + x \leqslant 0$

In Questions **22** to **26** list the solutions which satisfy the given conditions.

22. $3n < 30$; n is a positive integer (whole number).

23. $0 < a < 12$; a is an even number.

24. $\dfrac{3x}{5} < 7$; x is a positive integer.

25. $0 < 2y < 9$; y is an integer.

26. $\dfrac{p}{3} < 8$; p is a prime number.

27. State the smallest integer for which $5y > 21$.

28. Write down any value of x such that $2^3 < x < 3^2$.

29. Given that $1 \leqslant a \leqslant 10$ and $-5 \leqslant b \leqslant 6$, find

(a) the greatest possible value of $\dfrac{b}{a}$.

(b) the greatest possible value of $b^2 - a$.

(c) the greatest possible value of $a - b$

7.4 Simultaneous equations

Up to now the equations you have solved have had just one unknown. For example $\quad 3x - 1 = 1 - 4x$,

$$5(1 - x) = 2(3x + 1),$$

$$x(x + 1) = 100.$$

The equation $3x + y = 8$ involves two variables x and y. There are many pairs of values of x and y which satisfy the equation.
For example, if $x = 1$ and $y = 5$, $(3 \times 1) + 5 = 8$
or, if $x = 4$ and $y = -4$, $(3 \times 4) + (-4) = 8$.

There is in fact an infinite number of pairs of solutions. Similarly the equation $2x + 5y = 1$ is satisfied by an infinite number of pairs of solutions.

When we solve a *pair* of *simultaneous* equations we find the one pair of values of x and y which satisfy *both* equations simultaneously. Confirm that the equations $3x + y = 8$ and $2x + 5y = 1$ are both satisfied by $x = 3$ and $y = -1$.
These are the solutions of the simultaneous equations.

Graphical solution of simultaneous equations

The equations $\quad x + y = 7$ and
$$2x - y = -1$$

can be represented by straight lines as shown.

Since both lines pass through the point (2, 5), the solutions of the simultaneous equations

$$x + y = 7$$

$$2x - y = -1$$

are $x = 2$, $y = 5$.

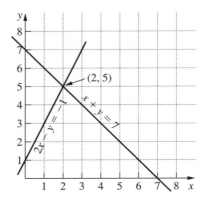

Solve the simultaneous equations

$$2x + y = 6$$
$$x - 2y = -2.$$

(a) Draw the line $2x + y = 6$.
When $x = 0$, $y = 6$
When $y = 0$, $x = 3$
When $x = 1$, $y = 4$

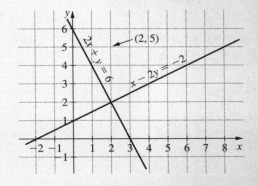

(b) Draw the line $x - 2y = -2$.
When $x = 0$, $y = 1$
When $y = 0$, $x = -2$
When $x = 6$, $y = 4$

(c) The lines intersect at $(2, 2)$ so
the solutions are $x = 2$, $y = 2$.

Exercise 1

1. Use the graph to solve the
simultaneous equations.

(a) $2x + y = 8$
$\quad x + y = 5$

(b) $x - y = -5$
$\quad x + y = 5$

(c) $2x + y = 8$
$\quad x - y = -5$

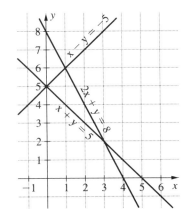

2. Use the graph to solve
the simultaneous equations.

(a) $\quad x + y = 11$
$\quad x + 3y = 13$

(b) $2x - y = -2$
$\quad x + y = 11$

(c) $x + 3y = 13$
$\quad 2x - y = -2$

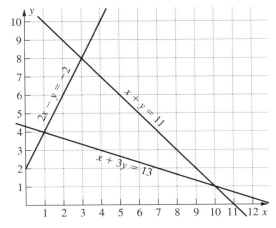

In Questions **3** to **8** solve the simultaneous equations by drawing graphs.

3. $x + y = 6$
$y = x + 3$
Draw axes with x and y from 0 to 6.

4. $x + 2y = 11$
$2x + y = 13$
Draw axes with x and y from 0 to 13.

5. $3x + 4y = 24$
$3x + 2y = 18$
Draw axes with x and y from 0 to 9.

6. $x + y = 5$
$y = x + 2$
Draw axes with x and y from 0 to 5.

7. $y = 3x + 6$
$x + y = 4$
Draw axes with x and y from -2 to 6.

8. $2x + 5y = 17$
$2x - 3y = -3$
Draw axes with x and y from 0 to 6.
[Give your answers correct to 1 d.p.]

9. Use the graph to solve the equations below. Give your answers correct to 1 d.p. where necessary.

(a) $x + y = 9$
$y = 2x - 3$

(b) $x + 3y = 5$
$x + y = 9$

(c) $x + 3y = 5$
$y = 2x - 3$

(d) $y = 2x - 3$
$5y = 4x + 18$

(e) $5y = 4x + 18$
$x + 3y = 5$

(f) $x + y = 9$
$5y = 4x + 18$

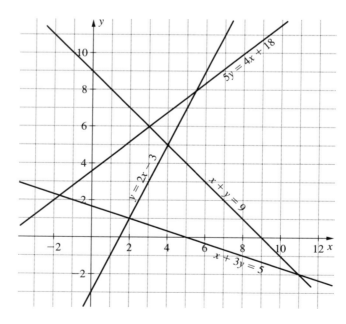

Algebraic solution of simultaneous equations

(a) Consider the simultaneous equations $\quad 5x + y = 21 \qquad [1]$

$$3x + y = 13 \qquad [2]$$

If we subtract equation [2] from equation [1] we eliminate the y terms.

We obtain $\qquad\qquad 2x = 8$

$$x = 4$$

Now substitute $x = 4$ into equation [1] (or equation [2]).

$$(5 \times 4) + y = 21$$

$$y = 1$$

The solution is $x = 4$, $y = 1$

(b) Consider the simultaneous equations $\quad x - y = 4 \qquad [1]$

$$4x + y = 31 \qquad [2]$$

If we *add* equation [1] to equation [2] we eliminate the y terms.

We obtain $\qquad\qquad 5x = 35$

$$x = 7$$

Now substitute $x = 7$ into equation [1] (or equation [2]).

$$7 - y = 4$$

$$y = 3$$

The solution is $x = 7$, $y = 3$.

Solve the simultaneous equations

(a) $x + 2y = 7 \qquad [1]$

$x - y = 4 \qquad [2]$

Label the equations [1] and [2]

$[1] - [2]$ gives $2y - (-y) = 3$

$$3y = 3$$

$$y = 1$$

Substitute $y = 1$ in [1]

$$x + (2 \times 1) = 7$$

$$x = 5$$

The solution is $x = 5$, $y = 1$.

(b) $3x + 2y = 10 \qquad [1]$

$5x - 2y = 14 \qquad [2]$

In this case to eliminate the y terms we *add* the equations.

$[1] + [2]$ gives $8x = 24$

$$x = 3$$

Substitute $x = 3$ in [1]

$$9 + 2y = 10$$

$$2y = 1$$

$$y = \tfrac{1}{2}$$

The solution is $x = 3$, $y = \tfrac{1}{2}$.

Remember: 'If the signs in front of the letter to be eliminated are the *same* we *subtract*, but if the signs are different we add.'

230

Exercise 2

Solve the simultaneous equations.

1. $5x + y = 22$
$2x + y = 10$

2. $6x + y = 31$
$3x + y = 16$

3. $5x + 2y = 16$
$x + 2y = 4$

4. $7x + 4y = 17$
$3x + 4y = 5$

5. $x + 3y = 11$
$x + 2y = 9$

6. $3x + 5y = 21$
$3x - y = 3$

In Questions **7** to **12** add the equations to eliminate the y terms.

7. $3x + y = 14$
$2x - y = 6$

8. $5x + 2y = 16$
$3x - 2y = 8$

9. $7x - 3y = 24$
$2x + 3y = 3$

10. $5x - y = -7$
$x + y = -5$

11. $6x - y = -26$
$5x + y = -18$

12. $x + 3y = -4$
$2x - 3y = -11$

Sometimes we cannot eliminate either x or y terms unless we multiply one equation or both equations by a suitable number or numbers. Examples (a) and (b) illustrate the method.

(a) $3x + y = 14$ [1]

$x + 2y = 3$ [2]

Multiply equation [1] by 2.

[1] × 2: $6x + 2y = 28$ [3]

[3] − [2]: $5x = 25$

          $x = 5$

Substitute $x = 5$ in [1] (or [2])

$(3 \times 5) + y = 14$

      $y = -1$

The solution is $x = 5$, $y = -1$

(b) $5x + 2y = 23$ [1]

$2x + 3y = 18$ [2]

Multiply both equations.

[1] × 3: $15x + 6y = 69$ [3]

[2] × 2: $4x + 6y = 36$ [4]

[3] − [4]: $11x = 33$

          $x = 3$

Substitute $x = 3$ in [1] (or [2])

$(5 \times 3) + 2y = 23$

      $y = 4$

The solution is $x = 3$, $y = 4$

Exercise 3

Solve the simultaneous equations.

1. $4x + y = 14$
$5x + 2y = 19$

2. $2x + y = 5$
$5x + 3y = 12$

3. $4x + 3y = 25$
$x + 5y = 19$

4. $7a + 2b = 22$
$3a + 4b = 11$

5. $5m + 3n = 11$
$4m + 6n = 16$

6. $2x + 3y = 20$
$x + 5y = 31$

In Questions **7** to **9** alter one of the equations and then add to eliminate the y terms.

7. $3x + 2y = 19$
$4x - y = 29$

8. $5x - y = 8$
$7x + 4y = 22$

9. $8x - 3y = 30$
$3x + y = 7$

In the remaining questions alter either one or both equations before eliminating the x or y terms.

10. $2x + 3y = 12$
$5x + 4y = 23$

11. $3x + 2y = 14$
$2x + 7y = 15$

12. $9a + 5b = 15$
$3a - 2b = -6$

13. $2x + 5y = 5$
$4x + 3y = 3$

14. $3x - 2y = 21$
$4x + 3y = 11$

15. $6x + 5y = 20$
$5x + 2y = 21$ Be careful!

16. $7x + 5y = 32$
$3x + 4y = 23$

17. $x - y = -1$
$2x - y = 0$

18. $y - x = -1$
$3x - y = 5$

19. $5x - 7y = 27$
$3x - 4y = 16$

20. $3x + 2y = 7$
$2x - 3y = -4$

21. $4x + 5y = -19$
$6x - 3y = 24$

22. $2x + 3y = 5$
$5x - 2y = -16$

23. $7a - 5b = 10$
$9a + 11b = -22$

24. $10x + 5y = 2\frac{1}{2}$
$7x - 2y = \frac{1}{10}$

Solving problems with simultaneous equations

Exercise 4

Solve the problems by forming a pair of simultaneous equations.
In Questions **1** to **4** there are two numbers to be found.

1. Find two numbers whose sum is 9 and which have a difference of 6. [Let the numbers be x and y.]

2. Twice one number plus the other number adds up to 13. The sum of the numbers is 10.

3. Double the larger number plus three times the smaller number makes 19. The difference between the numbers is 2.

4. The mean of the two numbers is 11. The larger number is one more than twice the smaller number.

5. Angle A is 12° greater than angle C. Find the angles of the triangle.

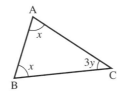

INDEX

School by a volcano

Gwynneth Ashby

Contents

1 The country of Japan

The country of Japan is made up of four large islands and hundreds of smaller ones. Kyushu is the largest of the southern islands. On Kyushu there is a town called Shimabara. Shimabara has six primary schools. One of them is called Number Three School.

The Sea of Japan is to the west of the four islands. The Pacific Ocean flows along the east coast. The island of Kyushu has several peninsulas jutting into the sea. A peninsula is a piece of land which has water on three sides. One of the peninsulas on Kyushu has the same name as the town. It is called the Shimabara Peninsula.

This book is about life on the Shimabara Peninsula and in Number Three School.

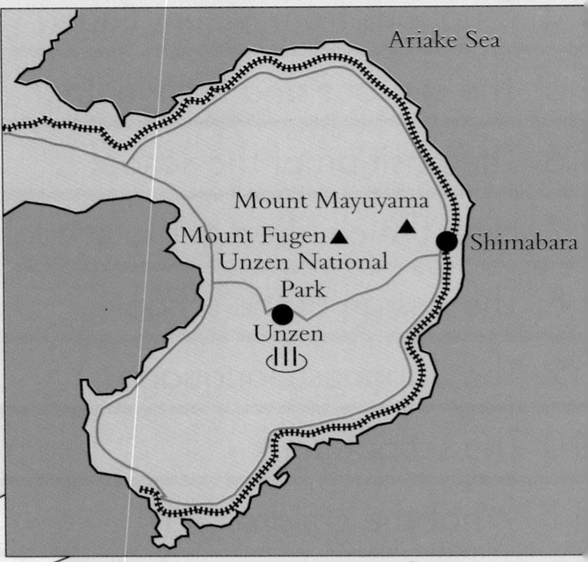

The Shimabara peninsula.

Ariake Sea

Mount Mayuyama
Mount Fugen ▲
Unzen National Park
Unzen
⑪⑫
Shimabara

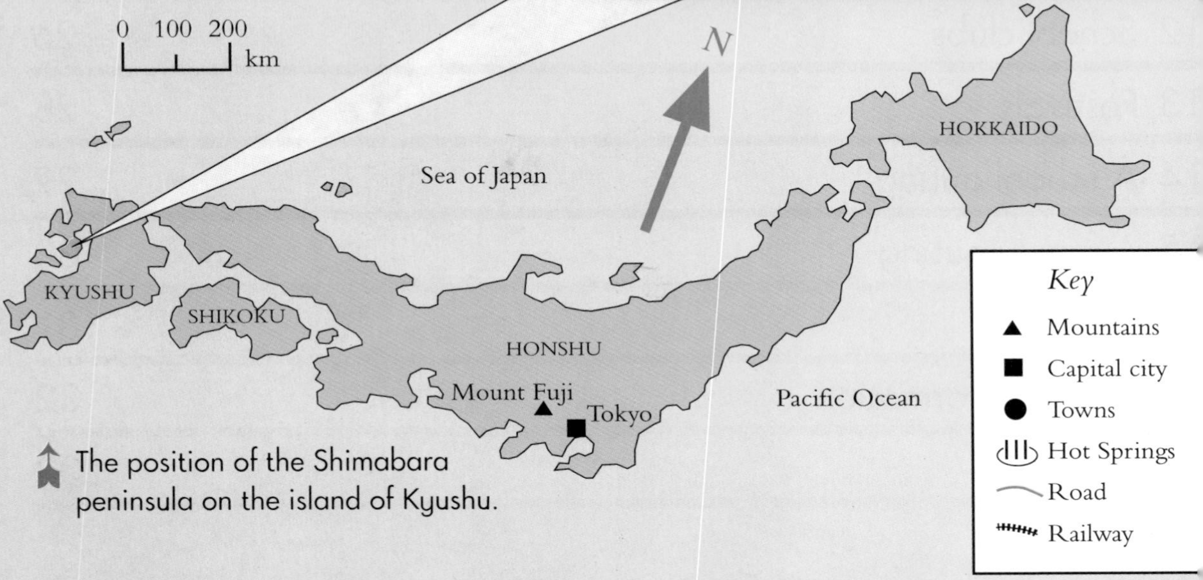

The position of the Shimabara peninsula on the island of Kyushu.

0 100 200
└──┴──┘ km

N

HOKKAIDO

Sea of Japan

KYUSHU
SHIKOKU
HONSHU
Mount Fuji ▲
Tokyo ■

Pacific Ocean

Key
▲ Mountains
■ Capital city
● Towns
⑪⑫ Hot Springs
⌒ Road
╫╫╫ Railway

2

2 The town of Shimabara

The town of Shimabara is about halfway along the east coast of the peninsula. It lies at the foot of two mountains. Mount Fugen, which is a volcano, is one of the mountains above the town. The other is called Mayuyama. Mount Mayuyama is in front of part of Fugen.

Shimabara has an old castle, Buddhist temples, and harbours with fishing boats. The town has a population of more than 40,000 people, and it is built round a bay called the Ariake Sea. Two car ferries and a high-speed boat leave from the main harbour to three ports in other parts of Kyushu.

Number Three School Song

In a spring wind we can call to Mayuyama
And Mayuyama will call us back.
This is primary school Number Three where
   we study proudly,
With the mountain behind us.

In front of us we have the Ariake Sea,
This is primary school Number Three where
   we study proudly,
With the sea watching over us.

3

3 What a volcano is like

The hard outside covering of the earth is called the crust. Underneath the crust, there are pools of boiling rock. A volcano is a mountain that has rock, ash, and gases coming from it through an opening.

Some of Japan's volcanic mountains are dormant, or sleeping. After two hundred years, dormant Mount Fugen in Unzen National Park has become active again. The boiling rock, known as magma, is pushing through a crater opening in the top of the mountain. When it reaches the air, magma is called lava. As lava cools, it becomes hard on the outside, but full of boiling liquid inside.

A lava dome on Mount Fugen.

Mount Fugen.

Lava domes

Lava and volcanic ash build up over the tops of the craters forming domes. When the domes become top-heavy, gases inside explode, and parts collapse. Mount Fugen does not have hot lava flowing down its sides. The danger to people, animals, and crops is caused by the clouds of red-hot ash, gases, and rocks which explode from the lava domes and pour down the mountainside.

Inside Mount Fugen

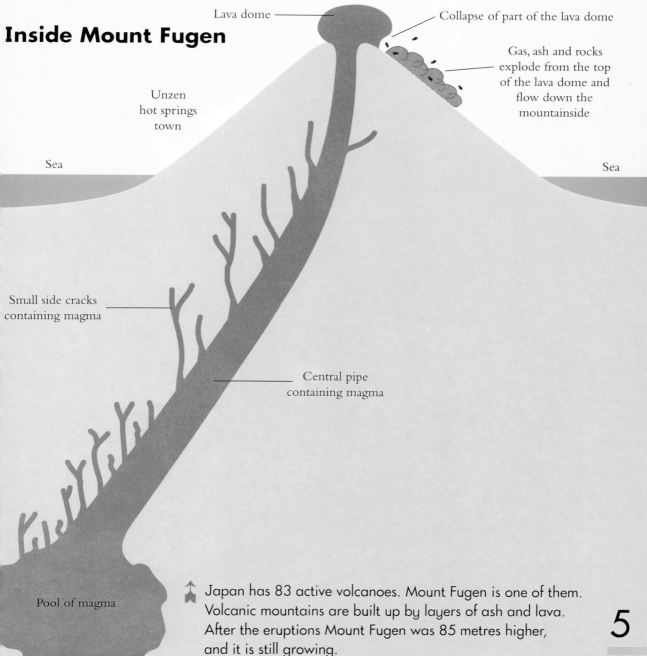

Lava dome

Collapse of part of the lava dome

Gas, ash and rocks explode from the top of the lava dome and flow down the mountainside

Unzen hot springs town

Sea

Sea

Small side cracks containing magma

Central pipe containing magma

Pool of magma

Japan has 83 active volcanoes. Mount Fugen is one of them. Volcanic mountains are built up by layers of ash and lava. After the eruptions Mount Fugen was 85 metres higher, and it is still growing.

5

4 Eruptions from Mount Fugen

Mount Fugen has recently become active again. Here is a newspaper account of one of the first eruptions in June 1991:

Hot ash and rocks burying a Buddhist temple.

Today, a lava dome on the top of Mount Fugen collapsed. Boulders as big as cars have come down the mountainside. The scorching ash and hot rocks have burnt houses, a school, and a forest. The hospitals are full of people being treated for burns.

During the daytime, parts of Shimabara became as black as night from the ash which fell like greyish-brown snow. Ash was blown to cities over 200 kilometres away.

Families evacuated from the danger zones are sleeping in Number Three school gymnasium. Prefabricated houses will be put up for them to live in. Vets are looking after their animals.

How warnings are given

People are told when there is going to be danger from the volcano. Warnings are given out on the radio and television.

- All districts have loudspeakers on high poles through which warnings can be broadcast.

- Each family has a small radio receiver. It is tuned in to a broadcasting studio at the town hall.

- Cable television cameras show what is happening to the volcano.

- Instruments at an observatory in the town measure the movement of magma as it rises to the surface through cracks in the crust. This movement causes underground earthquakes, although most of the them are too small for people to feel. Scientists at the observatory can usually tell when Mount Fugen is about to erupt from the strength and number of earthquakes shown on the print-out graphs.

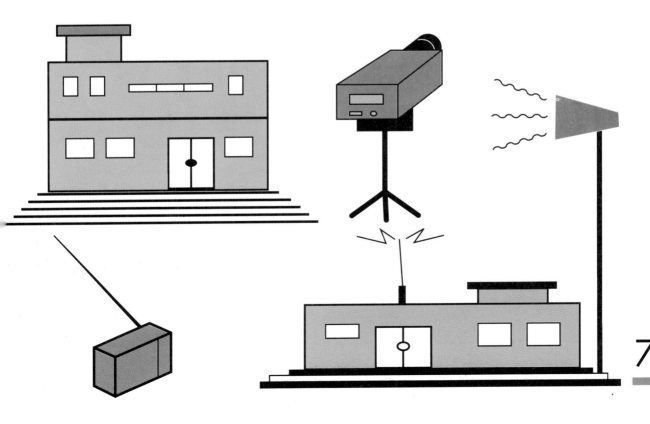

How the eruptions have affected the school

Children have to wear volcano helmets to school.

During ash falls, windows must be closed. Air-conditioners have been installed.

Part of the school playground has temporary classrooms. These were used for a time by the children of Number Five school. When Mount Fugen is less active, the prefabricated classrooms will be taken down.

In spite of the many problems caused by the volcano, the children are bright and cheerful. They are told not to panic and not to spread rumours.

 Wearing volcano helmets to school.

5 The seasons and the weather

Kyushu has four seasons. These are spring, summer, autumn and winter. There is a lot of rain during June and July. In the autumn, there are sometimes violent storms called typhoons.

The weather on the Shimabara Peninsula

In spring it is sunny, but not too hot. During the month of April, the cherry blossom comes out. Families have picnics under the cherry trees. Summer starts with heavy rain, and then it gets very hot. During the autumn there are often typhoons. These can cause a lot of damage.

In winter, the high slopes of the mountains may have frost and snow on them. January and February are the coldest months of the year.

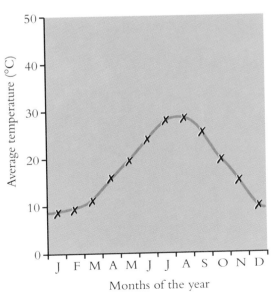

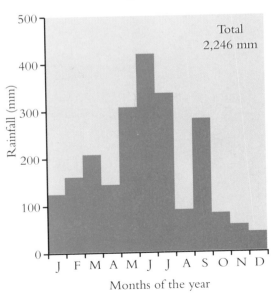

 Graph showing average temperatures in Shimabara.

 Bar chart showing average rainfall in Shimabara.

9

The summer – the rainy season

From about the second week in June until the middle of July, winds bringing rain blow across the Pacific Ocean. This is Kyushu's rainy season. Children take umbrellas to school – it is too hot and sticky to wear raincoats. Farmers plant out their rice seedlings during this rainy period.

August is the hottest month of the year, with many hours of sunshine. The air becomes very hot, so everyone turns up the air-conditioning. Some houses in Shimabara have solar panels on their roofs. The sun's energy heats the pipes inside the panels giving the household plenty of hot water for baths.

10

⬆ Rice seedlings are planted by hand or by machines.

The autumn – the typhoon season

September is the worst month for typhoons, although sometimes there are typhoons in August and October.

A typhoon is a tropical rainstorm which builds up over warm seas near the Equator. The heat which has been sucked up from the sea provides energy, and this drives the typhoon across the Pacific Ocean to the coast of Japan.

During a typhoon, violent winds can rip tiles from roofs, and bring down power lines and telephone wires. Shutters are fastened over windows and children are told to stay indoors. On Mount Fugen, heavy rain mixes with the volcanic ash and sometimes causes mud-slides. These mud-slides can cover roads, bend railway lines, and bury houses and cars.

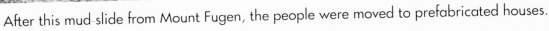
After this mud-slide from Mount Fugen, the people were moved to prefabricated houses.

6 The position of the school

Number Three school is on top of a little hill above a shopping street. More than six hundred children go to the school. They live on both sides of a main road, which is called Number 251. Most children live in Japanese-style houses with sliding doors and windows.

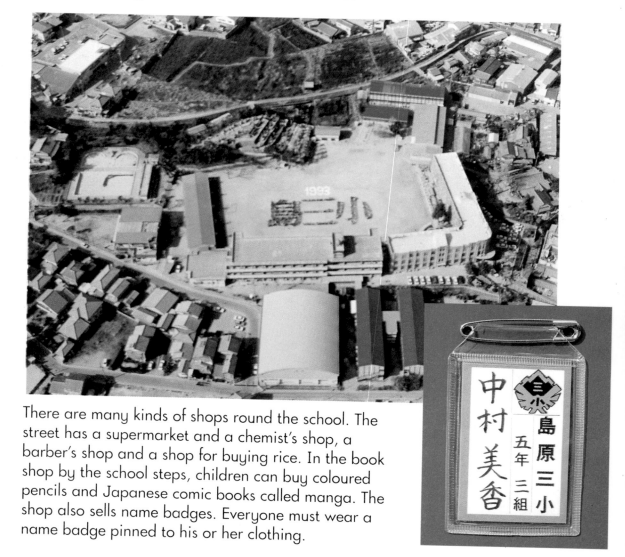

There are many kinds of shops round the school. The street has a supermarket and a chemist's shop, a barber's shop and a shop for buying rice. In the book shop by the school steps, children can buy coloured pencils and Japanese comic books called manga. The shop also sells name badges. Everyone must wear a name badge pinned to his or her clothing.

島原三小
五年 三組
中村美香

The school district

The small streets round the school do not have names, but each district has a map which shows the positions and the numbers of the houses. Some of the narrow streets to the south of road 251 lead to little harbours which have fishing boats in them. One of the streets has a playground and a community hall where children can play games when it is raining.

A single track railway line also goes through the streets. The train driver blows a hooter to warn people when the train is coming.

In this part of Shimabara, most children live in Japanese-style houses. The front doors are made of wood and glass, and the roofs have grey tiles.

 The roof on the left has a solar panel.

13

7 How the children get to school

Children in Japan start primary school at the age of six. They are not taken to school by their parents. In the morning, the children walk to school in groups. An older boy or girl is the leader of the group.

Primary school children are not allowed to ride bicycles to school. They have to walk. Most children who go to Number Three school live between five and twenty-five minutes' walk away. The group leader looks after the younger children, and holds up a yellow flag when they cross the road.

In Japan, nobody likes to be different from anyone else. The children all have the same type of school-bag. The boys have black bags and the girls have red bags.

 Walking home from school with a friend.

Neighbourhood groups

The school decides which roads and traffic crossings each group must use, and where the children are to meet. Sometimes the meeting-place is outside the group leader's house, sometimes it is at a safe spot like a shrine or a spring. Each group leader is in charge of up to ten children who come from homes close together in the neighbourhood. There are groups for boys and groups for girls. However long the walk, all the groups must be at school by eight o'clock.

In the afternoon, children walk home not with their group but with friends. This is because they finish school at different times. It is also safer at this time of day, because there is less traffic.

Children in Grade 1 wear yellow covers on their school-bags, to show that they are the youngest children in the school.

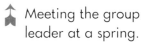 Meeting the group
leader at a spring.

15

8 The design of the school

There are three floors of classrooms in Number Three school. They are built round a large playground. In one corner there are slides and swings. On the opposite side, there is an animal house where chickens and rabbits are kept.

The classrooms for the younger children are on the ground floor. On this floor there is also a first aid room, an office, and rooms for the headteacher and the teachers. The school kitchen is on the ground floor. The other two floors have music and craft rooms, and classrooms for the older children.

There is a large gymnasium for indoor games and for Saturday morning school assemblies. The gymnasium is a separate building.

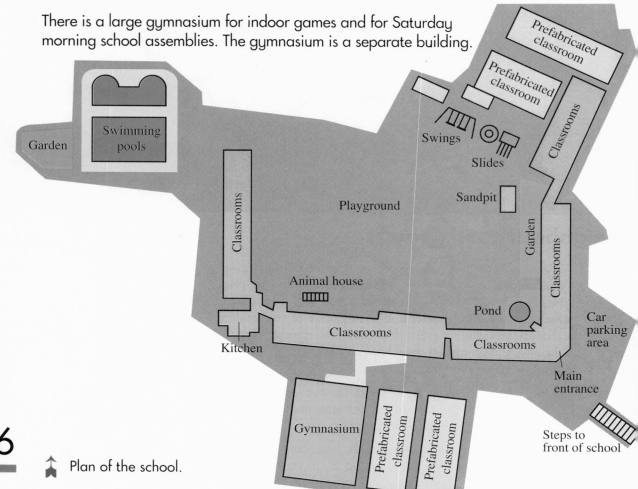

Plan of the school.

9 The Japanese language

It is difficult to read and to write the Japanese language. Children have to learn three different kinds of signs. These are called hiragana, katakana, and kanji.

Hiragana

Children first learn the 46 hiragana signs. Each sign stands for a syllable. When they start school, children in Grade 1 are taught to make their hiragana large. The word for bear in hiragana is kuma. It has two syllables.

The hiragana sign for the syllable 'ku' is

The hiragana sign for the syllable 'ma' is

Later, children make their hiragana smaller. Then they write kuma like this

Interesting facts

Sometimes Japanese is written in columns from the top of the page to the bottom of the page and from right to left. Sometimes it is written across the page from left to right, Western-style.

17

Katakana

The second set of 46 signs which children learn is called katakana. Katakana words are also made up of syllables. Katakana is used for writing foreign names and for words borrowed from other languages, particularly words for food.

Kanji

At primary school, children also learn to read and write about 1000 Chinese characters. These are called kanji. Many kanji look rather like pictures which show a meaning. A kanji may be a simple character with just a few strokes, or it may be complicated to write – with more than twenty strokes. When they go to senior school, children learn another 1000 kanji.

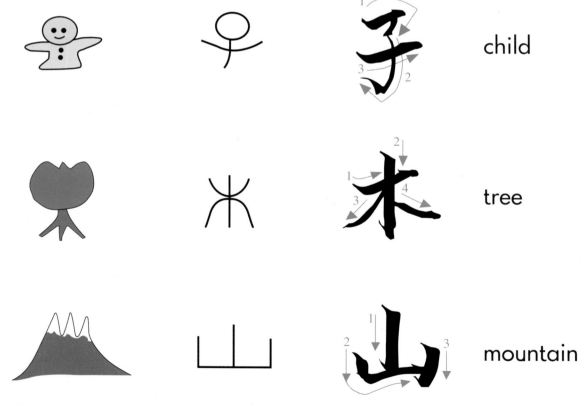

child

tree

mountain

 Kanji. The numbers show the order in which the strokes are written. The arrows show the direction.

Calligraphy

As well as writing kanji with a pen or pencil, the children have lessons on how to write Chinese characters with a brush and black ink. This is called calligraphy which means 'beautiful writing'. Calligraphy is used for special writing, like poetry and party invitations.

 The children practising calligraphy are writing the kanji for the word 'departure'.

19

10 The school day

Before the school day begins, and at the beginning and end of each lesson, children and teachers bow to each other. Everyone studies Japanese, mathematics and science. P.E., art and music are the children's favourite lessons.

P.E. lessons are held in the gym or out-of-doors. In the middle of June, swimming lessons begin in the school's open-air pools. Art lessons are held outside or in the classroom. In social studies, the children learn about the town they live in. Sometimes they go on to the school roof. They draw the castle, Mount Mayuyama, and the harbour.

Time	Lesson / Activity
8.05 – 8.30 a.m.	Classroom meeting. Children bow to teacher and say 'Ohayo gozaimasu' ('Good morning')
8.30 – 9.15 a.m.	Japanese
9.25 – 10.10 a.m.	Mathematics
10.20 a.m. – 12.05 p.m.	Art and craft
12.05 – 12.50 p.m.	Lunch time
12.50 – 1.35 p.m.	Play time
1.35 – 2.00 p.m.	Cleaning school time
2.00 – 2.45 p.m.	P. E.
2.45 – 3.00 p.m.	Classroom meeting. Children bow to teacher and say 'Sayonara' ('Good-bye')

 A typical day's lessons and activities for a pupil in Grade 3 (8–9 year olds). Every grade has homework.

Playing a pianica

The younger children learn to play musical notes on a pianica, which is a
type of keyboard. A pianica is played by blowing into a plastic mouthpiece
at the end of a tube. The tube is joined to the keyboard, and at the same
time as blowing down the tube, the children press the keys on the
keyboard. Pressing the key lets the air pass over the brass reed underneath
it. This makes the reed vibrate to produce a musical note.

Cleaning the school

To keep the building tidy, Japanese children clean their school each day. They also change from outdoor shoes into slippers when they go indoors. This helps to stop the corridors and classrooms from getting dirty. The older children work on committees. They think out ways of improving the school.

The children enjoy cleaning their school! They push the desks to the back of the classrooms, and they sweep the floors. Other groups clean the windows, wash the toilets, and put out new toilet rolls. Inside each block of toilets there is a row of plastic shoes. It is the custom to wear different shoes inside the toilet.

The playground is also tidied. The children collect the rubbish and burn it in an incinerator. Everyone takes pride in the school. There is no vandalism.

The children take it in turns to do the different cleaning jobs.

School committees

Before and after school, and during the midday break, children in Grades 5 and 6 work on different committees. The flower committee grows and plants out flowers for the school garden. The animal committee looks after the rabbits and hens, and feeds the fish.

The broadcasting committee plays music tapes and gives out notices. Primary school children are not allowed to wear their own watches to school. The broadcasting committee tells the children the time, and when they must stop playing and start cleaning the school.

There is also a library committee which lends out books, a lunch committee which writes up the day's menu, and a notice-board committee which puts up the children's paintings.

All these committees work to improve the life of the school.

The broadcasting committee at work.

The flower committee at work.

23

11 What the children eat

Everyone at Number Three school must have the midday meal. Some days the food is Japanese. On other days it is a Western kind of meal.

Several children from each grade fetch the food from the school kitchen. Sometimes it is a Japanese meal with rice, fish, pickled vegetables, and soup with seaweed. Sometimes it is a Western meal. Then there will be bread, meat and salad. When they have eaten, the children clean their teeth. Their brushes and toothpaste are kept in a box in the classroom.

↑ Children serving the food wear face masks.

The importance of eating meals together

Eating meals together is considered part of the school day. At mealtimes the pupils arrange their desks into groups of four or six. Every day the teacher sits with a different group. Before they start eating, the children say 'Itadakimasu', which means 'I gratefully receive'.

The older children also go with their teachers on overnight educational trips. Grade 5 school children walk in the mountains, and Grade 6 pupils visit different parts of Kyushu. These trips give other opportunities for the children to live and eat together in groups.

12 School clubs

Wednesday is school club day. Clubs are held after school. They last for an hour. Some children join the sports clubs. Other children make things or play board-games.

There are more than twenty clubs at Number Three school. Everyone in the top three grades must join one and stay in it for a year. Sports clubs are the favourite. There is a table tennis club and a girls' volley-ball club. There are also football and softball clubs. Softball is like baseball, but it is played with a softer and larger ball.

The softball club practising for the school match.

Craft Clubs

In the craft clubs, the children work at Japanese crafts. The girls dye T-shirts with vegetable dyes. The boys make wooden games, and paint them with bright colours. The boys play this game by trying to knock away the blocks under the dolls without making them fall.

The shogi club

Shogi is Japanese chess. It is played by two people. There are 81 squares on the board, and each player has 20 pieces. These are made up of nine pawns, a king, a rook and a bishop, two gold generals, two silver generals, two knights and two lances. There is no queen.

↑ The shogi club.

13 Festivals

There are two festivals in the year for children. March 3rd is called Girls' Day and May 5th is Boys' Day.

Girls' Day

On Girls' Day special dolls are arranged on shelves. They are dressed in Japanese clothing called kimonos. There are emperor and empress dolls, ladies-in-waiting, palace servants, and court musicians. These dolls are not played with – they are for display only.

Emperor and empress dolls and the court ladies.

Boys' Day

On Boys' Day children put model armour on the shelves. It is copied from the armour worn long ago by Japanese soldiers. Special festival cakes are eaten. These are white and sticky, and they are made from rice-flour. Inside, there is a sweet paste of cooked red beans.

Nowadays, Boys' Day is often called Children's Day.

14 A school outing

In April, Number Three school goes for a picnic. It is called the Welcome Picnic, and it is to welcome Grade 1 children to their new school.

The children, the headteacher and the teachers all walk a kilometre to a park near the school. The children carry bento in their rucksacks. Bento are lunch-boxes. Inside the bento there are chopsticks, and things to eat like rice, omelette, cooked fish, and sausages on sticks. After they have eaten, the children play football and other games.

After helping Grade 1 the older children have their picnic.

15 A family outing

Families often go for a day's outing to Unzen National Park. It takes about fifty minutes from Shimabara by car or bus. The town of Unzen has hot springs.

There are often hot springs near volcanoes. This is because magma, deep below the ground, heats up the underground water. This boiling water bubbles to the surface and makes pools and springs. Thick clouds of steam rise above the pools and come up through cracks in the ground.

Visitors can buy hard-boiled eggs which are cooked in the steam. A pipe is sunk into the ground, and the eggs are put in a basket and balanced over the steam.

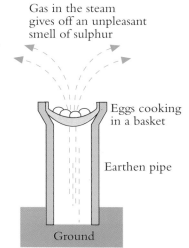

Gas in the steam gives off an unpleasant smell of sulphur

Eggs cooking in a basket

Earthen pipe

Ground

Unzen National Park

Parts of Unzen National Park are closed to visitors because of the eruptions from Mount Fugen. Everybody hopes that the eruptions will soon stop. Then visitors will be able to walk on the tracks around the volcano, and enjoy once again the scenery and the wild life in the whole of the National Park.

A path by one of the hot springs in the town of Unzen. ➡

30

Glossary

Air-conditioner	An air-conditioner is a metal box with equipment inside. This cleans and cools the air.
Calligraphy	Calligraphy in Japan is the writing of Chinese characters with a brush and black ink.
Committee	A committee is a group of people working together for some special purpose.
Crater	A crater is an opening in a volcano.
Crust	A crust is any hard outside covering, like the crust of the earth.
Earthquake	An earthquake is a shaking or sliding of the ground. Earthquakes are caused by movements deep within the earth.
Eruptions	Eruptions are breakings out. Volcanoes have eruptions of hot rock, ash and gases.
Evacuated	Evacuated means removed from danger.
Festival	A festival is a time for being happy and for the eating of special foods.
Incinerator	An incinerator is a furnace for burning rubbish.
Installed	When something is installed, it is put in a place or building so that it can be used.
Kimono	A kimono is a long, loose Japanese robe with wide sleeves, worn by both men and women.
Lava	Lava is hot, liquid rock flowing from a volcano. When the liquid rock cools and becomes solid, it is still called lava.
Magma	Magma is red-hot liquid rock found inside the earth underneath the crust.
Neighbourhood	A neighbourhood is everything which makes up a district–like people, shops, houses and parks.
Observatory	An observatory is a building with instruments. The instruments record facts about earthquakes, volcanic eruptions, the stars and other events of nature.
Peninsula	A peninsula is a piece of land which has water on three sides.
Prefabricated buildings	Prefabricated buildings are made in sections at a factory. They are fitted together at the place where they will be used.

Solar panel	A solar panel is a glass plate on top of a black metal box. The box contains pipes which are heated by the sun. The hot water goes from the roof into a tank inside the house.
Syllable	A syllable is a part of a word which can be pronounced on its own. Vol/ca/no is a word of three syllables, A/ri/a/ke is a word of four syllables.
Temporary	Temporary means something which lasts for only a short time.
Vandalism	Vandalism of buildings and possessions is damage which is done on purpose.
Vibrate	Vibrate means to move quickly backwards and forwards.
Volcanic ash	Volcanic ash is powdered lava. The lava is small, like grains of sand.

Further information

Books

The Story of the Earth – Volcano by Lionel Bender, Franklin Watts 1988

What Happens When Volcanoes Erupt? by Daphne Butler, Simon & Schuster Young Books 1993

Eyewitness Guides – Volcano by Susanna van Rose, Dorling Kindersley 1992

Volcanoes by Jenny Wood, Two-Can 1990